FILL THE SKY

McGRAW-HILL READING

FILL THE SKY

Authors

Elizabeth Sulzby
The University of Michigan

James Hoffman
University of Texas at Austin

Charles Mangrum II
University of Miami,
Coral Gables, Florida

Jerome Niles
Virginia Polytechnic Institute

Timothy Shanahan
University of Illinois at Chicago

William H. Teale
University of Texas at San Antonio

Arnold Webb
Research for Better Schools
Philadelphia, Pennsylvania

Literature Consultant

Sylvia Peña
University of Houston

Contributing Authors

Lillian K. Boyd
Detroit Public Schools

Bernard P. Floriani
Delaware State Supervisor for Reading

Kay M. Kincade
University of Oklahoma,
Norman, Oklahoma

Jacqueline Kiraithe de Córdova
California State University at Fullerton

Daniel R. Lawson
Ambler Avenue Elementary School,
Carson, California

Leon Lessinger, CEO
Health Champions, Inc.
Beverly Hills, California

George Mason
University of Georgia

Kathleen Naylor
Educational Consultant
Brea, California

Karen S. Urbschat
Wayne County Intermediate
School District, Michigan

McGraw-Hill School Division

New York   Oklahoma City   St. Louis   San Francisco   Dallas   Atlanta

The title of this book, "Fill the Sky," is taken from the poem "People" by Charlotte Zolotow.

Cover Illustration: Tom Powers

Grateful acknowledgment for permission to reprint copyrighted material, illustrations and photographs appearing in this book is made on pages 4 and 352 of this book, which is hereby made a part of this copyright page.

ISBN 0-07-042135-8

McGraw-Hill School Division
1200 Northwest 63rd Street
Oklahoma City, Oklahoma 73116-5712

3 4 5 6 7 8 9 0—8 9 7 6 5 4 3 2 1 0 9

Contents

Part One   Discoveries

◇ Award-winning
book or author

Part Two   Changes

Part Three

Other Times

◇ Award-winning
book or author

Part Four Other Places

Reading on Your Own

The steps in this plan can help you read better.

Before You Read

- Read the name of the story.
- Look at the pictures.
- Think about what you will read in the story.
- Think about what you already know about this kind of story.

As You Read

- ◆ Stop after every page.
- ◆ Think about what you have read so far.
- ◆ Think about what might come next.

Sometimes you may come to a word you don't know. Use these steps to understand the word.

1. Try saying the word out loud.
2. Read the words that come before and after the new word. They may give you a clue to the meaning of the new word.
3. Look up the word. Use the glossary at the back of the book, or use a dictionary.
4. Ask for help.

After You Read

- ◆ Use your own words to retell what you have read.
- ◆ Think of the most important things you read.

PART ONE

Discoveries

The world is so full of a number of things,
I'm sure we should all be as happy as kings.

Happy Thought
by Robert Louis Stevenson

◆

Everywhere you look, there are discoveries to be made. Each day we learn a little more about the world around us. In the stories that follow, you'll read about people who are learning new things and making discoveries about themselves. As you read, think: What discoveries of your own will you make?

Exploring Words About Discoveries

Starting with What You Know

When you think of discoveries, what ideas come to mind? The words in the box below tell about discoveries. Use these words and words of your own to answer the questions after the box.

invent	search	detective
examine	smart	curious
clever	explorer	find

What can these words tell you about discoveries? For example, can a detective make a discovery? When a person invents something, does he or she make a discovery? Can you think of any other words that could be added to the list above?

Building a Word Map

The word map shows how some of the words in the box above go together. Think about words you can add to the map. Use the words above and other words of your own.

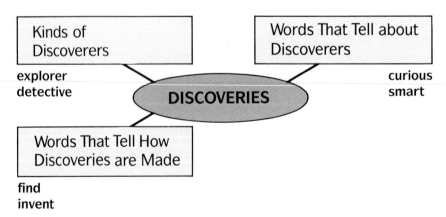

Kinds of Discoverers
explorer
detective

Words That Tell about Discoverers
curious
smart

DISCOVERIES

Words That Tell How Discoveries are Made
find
invent

Finishing a Story

The story below tells about two discoverers and a discovery they made. Some words are missing. Think of the words you would use to finish the story. Use the words from the box and word map in this lesson for ideas. Complete the story.

Jane and Dennis found an old treasure map. They were _____ children. They wanted to _____ the treasure.

"Let's become _____," said Jane. "Let's _____ the treasure." The map said the treasure was under a big rock. Jane and Dennis began to _____ the rock.

They found the rock and a note. It said:

"You are two _____ children. Come get your allowance."

The note was signed, "Dad."

Share your story with your classmates. How were the words you used different from the words your classmates used?

As You Read

In this part of the book, you will read about people and their discoveries. Keeping a Reader's Log will help you remember important thoughts, ideas, and words. As you read, make notes in your log. You could begin your Reader's Log with the word map. Add new words to the word map as you find them.

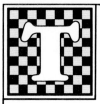
You never know what will happen when you try something new. In this fable by Aesop, the country mouse makes an important discovery when the town mouse invites her to the city for the first time.

THE TOWN MOUSE AND THE COUNTRY MOUSE

by Aesop

Once there was a mouse who was very contented with her life in the country. Then one day her friend, a town mouse who lived in the King's palace, came to visit.

The country mouse was very happy to see her friend. She fed her guest the best cheese and the finest seeds that she had. After their meal, the friends sat in the cozy cottage and chatted.

"Really, my dear," said the town mouse, "I am amazed that you seem so happy! It is so dull here and you have such plain food to eat."

"You must come see the elegance of the palace with me. There is fine food and dancing and excitement all the time. Please say you will come!"

The country mouse did not know what to say. She told her friend that she would need a week to decide. The next week passed quickly. "Are you coming home with me?" the town mouse asked her friend. "Life in town is an experience that should not be missed."

The country mouse agreed to go with her friend, and they traveled to town together.

It was late in the evening when the two little mice reached the palace. They were very hungry after their long trip, so they were delighted to find the remains of an elegant dinner in the King's dining hall. There were puddings and pies and breads and meats of every kind. The cheese was the finest.

But before the two mice had a chance to begin their meal, they heard the heavy steps of human beings. The poor country mouse was very frightened. The King's servants burst into the room and took all the wonderful food away.

The town mouse ran to the safety of her hole. The poor country mouse however, did not know what to do. She hid as best she could behind the thick leg of the couch. Trembling, she stayed there until all the footsteps faded away and the room was quiet again.

"Ah me, this elegant living is filled with dangers!" cried the country mouse. "I will not stay here one moment longer! I could not enjoy this fine house and this fine food. I know now only the peace of my country life can ease my worried heart!"

The town mouse asked her friend to stay, but the country mouse said no. She had seen enough of town life and quickly traveled home.

She raced through the night . . . and she did not rest until she reached her own front door. That night, a very contented little country mouse slept in her own quiet little cottage.

Thinking About the Theme

1. There are many good things about both the city and the country. Which do you like best?

2. When you go to a new place for the first time, there is always something new to discover. Can you think of a place that you would like to visit?

COMPREHENSION
◄BUILDER►

for **A Curve in the River** and
Through Grandpa's Eyes

Understanding Cause and Effect

Starting with What You Know

What happened in the second picture? Now look at the first picture. It tells you why the vase fell. It fell because the cat knocked over the vase.

Thinking About Cause and Effect

Sometimes one thing happens because something else has happened first. Read this next sentence. *Our shoes got wet because it was raining.* What happened? *Our shoes got wet.* Why did this happen? *This happened because it was raining.* The part of the sentence that tells what happened is called the **effect**. The part that tells why something happened is called the **cause**. A sentence that gives a cause and effect often has a clue word such as *because* or *so*.

A story might give two causes for one effect. Look at the following example.

Jenny woke up early. Today she was going to be in the class play. It was also her birthday.

What happened? Jenny woke up early. This is the effect. What two things made this effect happen? Jenny is going to be in the class play and today is her birthday. These are the two causes.

Practice

Read each sentence. Find the cause or causes and effect in each one. Tell what the clue word is.

1. The ice cubes melted because they were left out on the table.

2. The doorbell rang so Dad went to answer it.

3. We enjoyed reading the story because it was interesting and it made us laugh.

As You Read

Figuring out why things happen in a story will help you better understand what you are reading. Look for actions and events in the story that might be causes and effects. As you read, ask yourself these questions:

- What happened? Why did it happen?
- Are there clue words such as *because* or *so* that show the cause and effect?
- Is what happened a cause? What might its effect be?
- Is what happened an effect? What might its cause be?

Apply what you know about cause and effect as you read the two selections that follow. Use the side notes to help you.

When Julian sends a message in a bottle down the river, he dreams of the places he'll see and the discoveries he'll make. Faraway places are exciting, but Julian still has discoveries to make at home.

A Curve in the River

by Ann Cameron

This is something I learned in school: The whole body is mostly water.

We think we're solid, but we're not. You can tell sometimes from your blood and tears and stuff that what you're like inside isn't what you're like outside, but usually you'd never know.

Also, the whole earth is mostly water—three-quarters ocean. The continents are just little stopping places. And using water—streams and rivers and oceans—anybody could put a message in a bottle and send it all the way around the world.

That was my secret project.

I had a bottle with a cork. I had paper and a ballpoint pen. I wrote a message: *Whoever finds this bottle, please write or call me and tell me where you found it.*

This is what Julian wants to happen.

22

23

Julian throws the bottle in the water. Notice what the effect of this action is.

These are the reasons why Julian wants his project to work.

I put down my address and phone number. Then I corked the bottle and carried it down to the river.

I threw the bottle as far out as I could. It splashed, bobbed up and floated. I watched it go out of sight.

I kept thinking about my secret project.

Maybe my bottle was on the way to Hawaii.

Maybe it was on the way to France.

Maybe it was on the way to China.

Maybe I would write letters to the person who found it, and we would become friends. I would go visit the person where he or she lived.

I could see myself in Rio de Janeiro, dancing in the streets.

I could see myself in India, riding on an elephant.

I could see myself in Africa, taming wild lions.

A week went by.

I wondered how long I'd have to wait before I heard from the person who got my bottle. It might be months.

Maybe my bottle would go to the North Pole and be found stuck in the ice by Eskimo hunters. Then I realized it might lie in the ice for years before it was found. Somebody might phone or write me, and I would even have forgotten about my bottle.

I decided I should write a note to myself and hide it in my desk, where I would find it when I grew up, so I could remind myself about the bottle then.

Dear Old Julian, I wrote. *Remember the bottle you threw in the river?* And then I put down the day and the year that I threw it in.

24

I had just finished hiding this message in the back of my desk when the phone rang.

It was Gloria.

"Julian, I have some news!" she said.

"Oh, really?" I said. Nothing could be important news that wasn't about my bottle.

"Julian," Gloria said, "it's about your bottle with the message—I found it."

She sounded happy. I wasn't. My bottle was supposed to travel around the world.

Think about why Julian isn't happy.

"Julian?" Gloria said.

I didn't answer.

All that water to travel! All those countries to see! The whole world full of strangers! And where did my stupid bottle go? To Gloria's house!

"Julian?" Gloria said. "Are you still there?"

I couldn't talk. I was too disgusted.

I hung up.

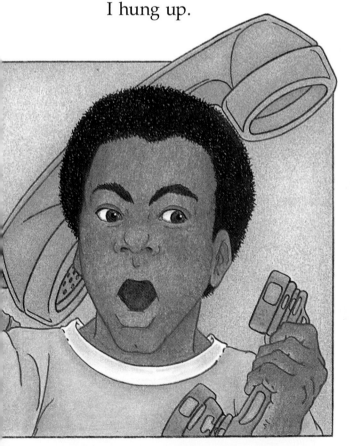

Gloria came looking for me.

"Tell her I'm not here," I said to Huey.

Huey went to the door. "Julian says he's not here," Huey said.

Notice what Huey says to Gloria. Think about how this causes Gloria to act and feel.

"Oh," Gloria said. She went away.

In a couple of days my father started noticing.

"I haven't seen Gloria lately," he said.

"I don't want to see her," I said.

"Why?" my father said.

"Because."

Then I decided to tell my father about the bottle and how Gloria found it. It didn't matter anymore to keep it a secret. The secret was over.

"That's too bad," my father said. "But it's not Gloria's fault."

"She found the bottle," I said. "She must be laughing at me for trying such a stupid idea."

"It's not a stupid idea," my father said. "You just had bad luck. You know what your problem is? It's the curve in the river. Your bottle got stuck on that curve, and it didn't have a chance."

Now Julian knows why the bottle got stuck. Predict what he might do.

I felt a little better. I went to see Gloria.

"I wanted to give you your bottle back," Gloria said. Then she added, "I thought it was a great idea, sending a message in a bottle."

"Well, it's a good idea, but it's a no-good idea because of the curve in the river. The bottle couldn't get around it," I explained.

"I guess it couldn't," Gloria said.

"Julian," my father said, "I have to make a long trip in the truck Saturday. I have to pick up some car parts. I'm going to go past the big bridge down the river. Would you like to ride along?"

I said I would.

"You know," my father said, "there's something we could do. We could walk out on the bridge. And if you wanted, you could send a new message. Your bottle would have a good chance from there. It's past the curve in the river."

I thought about it. I decided to do it. And I told my father.

"You know," he said, "if you don't mind my advice—put something special about yourself in the bottle, for the person who finds it."

"Why?" I asked.

"It'll give the wind and the water something special to carry. If you send something you care about, it might bring you luck."

Julian tries again. Predict what the effect might be.

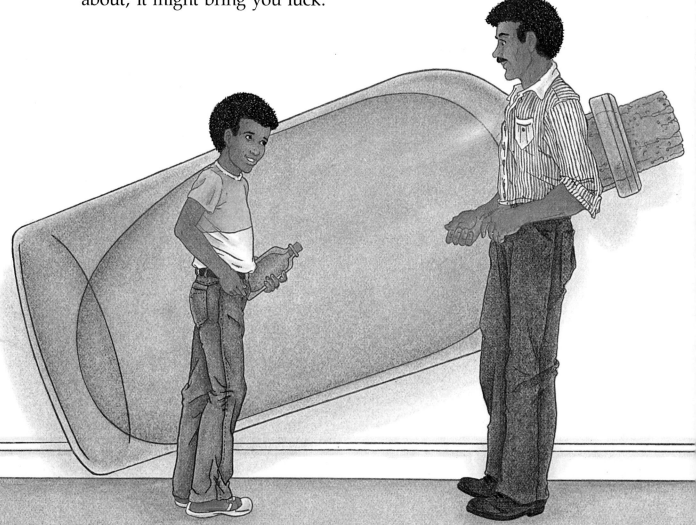

Think about what has caused Julian to change his mind.

I was working on my new message. And then I thought about Huey and Gloria. I thought how they might want to send bottles too. It didn't seem so important anymore that I be the only one to do it.

And that's what we did. We all got new bottles, and we put something special in each one. We each made a picture of ourselves for our bottle.

And in his, Huey put his favorite joke:
Where does a hamburger go on New Year's Eve?
To a meat ball.

In hers, Gloria put instructions on doing a cartwheel. In mine, I wrote instructions for taking care of rabbits.

We added our addresses and phone numbers and pushed in the corks tightly. We were ready for Saturday.

The bridge was long and silver and sparkled in the sun. It was so big that it looked like giants must have made it, that human beings never could have. But human beings did.

My father parked below the bridge. "From here we have to walk," he said.

We got out of the truck, which always smells a little bit of dust, but mostly of the raisins Dad keeps on the dashboard.

We walked in the outside walkers' lane to the middle of the river. Cars whizzed past. We each had our bottle in a backpack.

The bridge swayed a little. We could feel it vibrate. My father held Gloria's and Huey's hands. I held Gloria's other hand.

"It's scary, but it's safe," my father said.

28

We held on to the bridge railing and looked over the side. The green water slid under us very fast. For a minute it seemed like the bridge was moving and the water was standing still.

We unpacked our bottles.

"Don't just throw them over the side," my father said. "Make some wishes. Sending messages around the world is a big thing to do. Anytime you do a big thing, it's good to make wishes."

We did.

I don't know what Huey or Gloria wished. I wished our bottles would sail along together. I wished they wouldn't get trapped in seaweed or ice, or hit rocks. I wished we'd make new friends on the other side of the world. I wished we'd go to meet them someday.

"Ready?" my father said.

Together we threw our bottles over the side. They made a tiny splash. They looked very small, but we could see them starting toward the ocean.

They were like Columbus's ships. I hoped they'd stay together a long, long time.

A Reader Says

Julian should have sent more than one bottle. Then they could have gone to different places.

How did you feel about the story?

After You Read

Thinking About What You Read

1. How do you know that Julian has a good imagination?
2. Why do you think Julian acted the way he did when Gloria found the bottle?
3. What do you think Julian discovered about himself after he became annoyed with Gloria?
4. Why do you think Julian wished for the bottles to sail along together?

Thinking About How You Read

How did knowing about cause and effect help you understand why Julian was upset when Gloria found his bottle?

Sharing and Listening

Suppose you were Julian. Would you put instructions on how to care for rabbits in your bottle? What special thing would you put in your bottle? Share your ideas with your classmates. Listen carefully to their opinions.

Writing

Suppose you were to discover Julian's bottle. Write a short letter to Julian telling of your discovery and about yourself.

Where Go The Boats?

Dark brown is the river,
　　Golden is the sand.
It flows along forever,
　　With trees on either hand.

Green leaves a-floating,
　　Castles of the foam,
Boats of mine a-boating—
　　Where will all come home?

On goes the river
　　And out past the mill,
Away down the valley,
　　Away down the hill.

Away down the river,
　　A hundred miles or more,
Other little children
　　Shall bring my boats ashore.

Robert Louis Stevenson

When you put yourself in someone else's shoes, you try to understand how it feels to be that person. John tries looking at things the way his Grandpa does and makes many interesting discoveries about the world.

 THROUGH GRANDPA'S EYES

by Patricia MacLachlan

Of all the houses that I know, I like my grandpa's best. My friend Peter has a new glass house with pebble-path gardens that go nowhere. And Maggie lives next door in an old wooden house with rooms behind rooms, all with carved doors and brass doorknobs. They are fine houses. But Grandpa's house is my favorite. Because I see it through Grandpa's eyes.

Grandpa is blind. He doesn't see the house the way I do. He has his own way of seeing.

In the morning, the sun pushes through the curtains into my eyes. I burrow down into the covers to get away, but the light follows me. I give up, throw back the covers, and run to Grandpa's room.

The sun wakes Grandpa differently from the way
it wakes me. He says it touches him, *warming* him
awake. When I peek around the door, Grandpa is
already up and doing his morning exercises. He
stops and smiles because he hears me.

"Good morning, John."

"Where's Nana?" I ask him.

"Don't you know?" he says, bending and
stretching. "Close your eyes, John, and look
through my eyes."

I close my eyes. Down below, I hear the banging
of pots and the sound of water running that I
didn't hear before.

"Nana is in the kitchen," I say.

When I open my eyes again, I can see Grandpa nodding at me. He is tall with dark gray hair. And his eyes are sharp blue even though they are not sharp seeing.

I exercise with Grandpa. Up and down. Then I try to exercise with my eyes closed.

"One, two," says Grandpa, "three, four."

"Wait!" I cry. I am still on one, two when Grandpa is on three, four.

I fall sideways. Three times. Grandpa laughs as he hears my thumps on the carpet.

"Breakfast!" calls Nana from downstairs.

"I smell eggs frying," says Grandpa. He bends his head close to mine. "And buttered toast."

The wooden banister on the stairway has been worn smooth from Grandpa running his fingers up and down. I walk behind him, my fingers following Grandpa's smooth path.

We go into the kitchen.

"I smell flowers," says Grandpa.

"What flowers?" I ask.

He smiles. He loves guessing games.

"Not violets, John, not peonies . . ."

"Carnations!" I cry. *I* love guessing games.

"Silly." Grandpa laughs. "Marigolds. Right, Nana?"

Nana laughs, too.

"That's too easy," she says, putting two plates of food in front of us.

"It's not too easy," I protest. "All the smells mix together in the air."

"Close your eyes, John," says Nana. "Tell me what breakfast is."

"I smell the eggs. I smell the toast," I say, my eyes closed. "And something else. The something else doesn't smell good."

"*That* something else," says Nana, smiling, "is the marigolds."

When he eats, Grandpa's plate of food is a clock.

"Two eggs at nine o'clock and toast at two o'clock," says Nana. "And a dollop of jam."

"A dollop of jam," I tell Grandpa, "at six o'clock."

I make my plate of food a clock, too, and eat through Grandpa's eyes.

After breakfast, I follow Grandpa's path through the dining room to the living room, to the window that he opens to feel the weather outside, and to his cello in the corner.

"Will you play your cello with me, John?" he asks.

He tunes our cellos without looking. I play with a music stand and music before me. I know all about sharps and flats. I see them on the music. But Grandpa plays them. They are in his fingers. For a moment I close my eyes and play through Grandpa's eyes. My fingering hand slides up and down the cello neck—toward the pegs for flats, toward the bridge for sharps. But with my eyes closed my bow falls from the strings.

"Listen," says Grandpa. "I'll play a piece I learned when I was your age. It was my favorite."

He plays the tune while I listen. That is the way Grandpa learns new pieces. By listening.

"Now," says Grandpa. "Let's do it together."

"That's fine," says Grandpa as we play. "But C sharp, John," he calls to me. "C sharp!"

Later, Nana joins us.

"The river is up," she says.

Grandpa nods a short nod. "It rained again last night. Did you hear the gurgling in the rain gutter?"

Grandpa and I walk outside, through the front yard and across the field to the river. Grandpa has not been blind forever. He remembers in his mind the gleam of the sun on the river, the Queen Anne's lace in the meadow, and every dahlia in his garden. But he gently takes my elbow as we walk so that I can help show him the path.

"I feel a south wind," says Grandpa.

I can tell which way the wind is blowing because I see the way the tops of the trees lean. Grandpa tells by the feel of the meadow grasses and by the way his hair blows against his face.

When we come to the riverbank, I see that Nana was right. The water is high and has cut in by the willow tree. It flows around and among the roots of the tree, making paths. Paths like Grandpa's on the stair banister. I see a blackbird with a red patch on its wing sitting on a cattail. Without thinking, I point my finger.

"What is that bird, Grandpa?" I ask excitedly.

"*Conk-a-ree,*" the bird calls to us.

"A red-winged blackbird," says Grandpa promptly.

He can't see my finger pointing. But he hears the song of the bird.

"And somewhere behind the blackbird," he says, listening, "a song sparrow."

40

I hear a scratchy song, and I look and look until I see the earth-colored bird that Grandpa knows is here.

Nana calls from the front porch of the house.

"Nana's made hot bread for lunch," he tells me happily. "And spice tea." Spice tea is his favorite.

I close my eyes, but all I can smell is the wet earth by the river.

As we walk back to the house, Grandpa stops suddenly. He bends his head to one side, listening. He points his finger upward.

"Honkers," he whispers.

I look up and see a flock of geese, high in the clouds, flying in a V.

"Canada geese," I tell him.

"Honkers," he insists. And we both laugh.

We walk up the path again and to the yard where Nana is painting the porch chairs. Grandpa smells the paint.

"What color, Nana?" he asks. "I cannot smell the color."

"Blue," I tell him, smiling. "Blue like the sky."

"Blue like the color of Grandpa's eyes," Nana says.

When he was younger, before I can remember, before he was blind, Grandpa did things the way I do. Now, when we drink tea and eat lunch on the porch, Grandpa pours his own cup of tea by putting his finger just inside the rim of the cup to tell him when it is full. He never burns his finger. Afterward, when I wash the dishes, he feels them as he dries them. He even sends some back for me to wash again.

"Next time," says Grandpa, pretending to be cross, "I wash, you dry."

In the afternoon, Grandpa, Nana, and I take our books outside to read under the apple tree. Grandpa reads his book with his fingers, feeling the raised Braille dots that tell him the words.

As he reads, Grandpa laughs out loud.

"Tell us what's funny," says Nana. "Read to us, Papa."

And he does.

Nana and I put down our books to listen. A gray squirrel comes down the trunk of the apple tree, tail high, and seems to listen, too. But Grandpa doesn't see him.

After supper, Grandpa turns on the television. I watch, but Grandpa listens, and the music and the words tell him when something is dangerous or funny, happy or sad.

Somehow, Grandpa knows when it is dark, and he takes me upstairs and tucks me into bed. He bends down to kiss me, his hands feeling my head.

"You need a haircut, John," he says.

Before Grandpa leaves, he pulls the light chain above my bed to turn out the light. But, by mistake, he's turned it on instead. I lie for a moment after he's gone, smiling, before I get up to turn off the light.

Then, when it is dark for me the way it is dark for Grandpa, I hear the night noises that Grandpa hears. The house creaking, the birds singing their last songs of the day, the wind rustling the tree outside my window.

Then, all of a sudden, I hear the sounds of geese overhead. They fly low over the house.

"Grandpa," I call softly, hoping he has heard them too.

"Honkers," he calls back.

"Go to sleep, John," says Nana.

Grandpa says her voice smiles to him. I test it.

"What?" I call to her.

"I said go to sleep," she answers.

She says it sternly. But Grandpa is right. Her voice smiles to me. I know. Because I'm looking through Grandpa's eyes.

A Reader Says

By sharing the way he sees things with John, John's Grandpa probably appreciates the world more, too.

How did you feel about the story?

After You Read

Thinking About What You Read

1. How do you think Grandpa is able to see with his senses of hearing, touching, and smelling?
2. Why do you think Nana prepares Grandpa's plate like a clock?
3. How do you know that Grandpa and John have a good relationship?
4. How does seeing through Grandpa's eyes help John to discover things?

Thinking About How You Read

How did knowing about cause and effect help you understand how Grandpa ''saw'' things in the way he did?

Sharing and Listening

What important thing did you discover about blind people from reading this story? Share your thoughts with your classmates. Listen carefully as they share their thoughts.

Writing

Can you think of a time when an older person helped you to make a discovery of some kind? Write a paragraph in which you describe your experience.

Understanding Mysteries

Starting with What You Know

In some stories, you can guess what will happen and how the story will end. In other stories, you cannot. You are often surprised by the ending. What story have you read or heard that is like this?

One kind of story in which you might be surprised by the ending is a **mystery** story. This kind of story has a secret, and you must read carefully to try to figure out the secret and solve the mystery. Details in the story that help you solve the mystery are called **clues**.

Thinking About Mysteries

Mystery stories are made-up stories, or fiction. They have the same parts that all fiction has.

Characters: These are the people or animals in the story. They have a problem or goal.

Setting: This is the place where the story happens.

Plot: This is the important series of events that make up the story.

Outcome: This is the way the story ends. Usually, it shows the way the characters solve the problem or reach the goal.

In a mystery story, there is always a problem to solve. The writer describes something that has happened and tells how one character or two characters try to solve the problem. As a reader, you try to solve the mystery, too. The writer gives you clues but they are often hidden clues. You have to read and think carefully.

Before You Read

Think about the title of the story. Often the title gives you a clue about the mystery. Plan to look for clues as you read the story.

As You Read

Stop after every page. Think about what you have read so far. Ask yourself these questions as you read. The questions with blue diamonds are for any type of fiction. The questions with red diamonds are for mysteries.

Characters: ◆ Who are the characters?
◆ Which one will probably solve the mystery?

Setting: ◆ Where does the story happen?
◆ Is there something about the setting that is a clue to solving the mystery?

Plot: ◆ What is happening in the story?
◆ What clues do the actions lead to?

Outcome: ◆ How does the story end?
◆ What were the clues that solved the mystery?

Apply what you know about reading mysteries as you read the two mystery selections that follow. Use the side notes to help you.

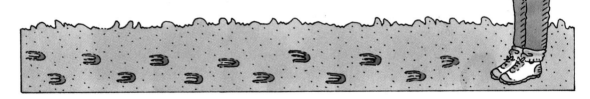

When Stan and Judy discover an old letter in Judy's cabin, they have no idea what's in store for them. Read to see how one discovery can lead to another.

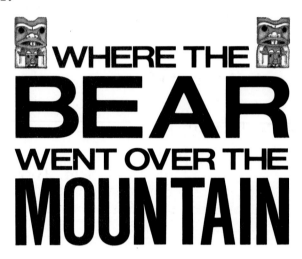

WHERE THE BEAR WENT OVER THE MOUNTAIN

by Blaine G. Goodman

Here are the main characters.

As Judy reached for the matches above the stone fireplace of the log cabin where she and her father had just moved, a letter fluttered to the floor. Her friend Stan, who was visiting, got to it first and exclaimed, "Look at the German stamp!"

48

"You can have it," said Judy, "but what's written in the letter?"

Stan removed some yellow paper from the envelope and read the letter out loud:

July 28, 1977

Dear Jim,

When I first came to Germany, I did not intend to stay, but I've changed my mind. I concealed all the Indian artifacts in the cave where I found them, and I put the artifacts from the gold-rush days with them. Thought they'd be safe there until you moved into the cabin.

Now, if you intend to open a store, the artifacts are all yours, or if not, just leave them. If someone can locate the cave "where the bear went over the mountain," well, finders keepers.

Yours, Bill

This sets up the mystery. Remember this clue.

"I'd really enjoy finding those gold-rush things," Stan remarked. "Do you think we can find them?"

"That was years ago," said Judy. "I bet that man Jim found them."

"Maybe," said Stan, "but we could look."

"But how do we find 'where the bear went over the mountain'?" asked Judy.

"I don't know," said Stan, "but maybe your Dad can examine the letter and help us."

They showed the letter to Judy's father; however, he just put the letter back into the envelope and shook his head, remarking, "This isn't bear country, so I don't know what this letter means."

Now you know more about the setting. Think about what kind of bear Bill could have meant.

Judy thought Mr. Curry would possibly know about Jim and the cave, so they went to search for him. In a few minutes they were in the old man's log cabin, waiting anxiously for his opinion. After he'd read the letter, he said, "Although your dad is right, in my opinion the story is true, and I remember Jim. He talked about opening a store, but one day he just left, and I never saw him again."

"Maybe we ought to begin searching for a cave," said Judy.

"Before you do," said Mr. Curry, "would you bring me some firewood? There's a pile of logs up the road, and you can fill your sacks with them. Don't try to carry them though. Just drag them."

Judy and Stan went to the firewood pile and began to fill the sacks. The sun was setting when Judy glanced up from her work.

Suddenly she shouted, "Look!"

"What's the matter?" asked Stan.

Judy pointed to a cluster of low mountains. When Stan looked, his eyes got big with surprise.

One of the low mountains had some unusual rocks on it and, as the sun set, it cast a shadow against another, larger mountain. The shadow looked like it was moving over the larger mountain.

"It looks like—a bear!" Stan shouted.

"What do you know about that!" said Judy.

"It's our bear," Stan said, "and tomorrow morning we ought to hike up the mountain and locate that cave. We'll know right where to search for it."

Judy and Stan are on the right track.

This is an important clue.

50

Both children arose early the next morning and dressed rapidly. They hiked up the low mountain toward the unusual rocks. When they finally reached the rock that had cast the shadow of the bear, Stan shook his head, saying, "Although this is the place, it doesn't look as if there's a cave around here."

Judy moved aside some bushes and crawled around a big rock. When she was safe on the other side, she pushed aside the rock, which hurtled down the mountain.

Judy seems to know what she is doing.

She suddenly pointed to where the rock had been and said, "It concealed the opening of the cave."

They both peered excitedly into the cave, and Stan shouted, "There it is!" He pointed at two big black boxes.

Predict what will be in the boxes.

Stan and Judy dragged the boxes from the cave, and then they dragged them home.

51

They opened the boxes and found the Indian and gold-rush artifacts Bill had written about. At the bottom of one box, Judy found a small leather bag and asked, "What's this?"

Stan glanced up and said, "That's a leather bag made to hold gold nuggets."

Judy examined the bag, turned it over, and poured several rust-brown rocks into her hand. Gold spots dotted the rocks. "They're gold nuggets!" shouted Judy.

"And to think," Stan said, "you didn't know if you'd enjoy being here on the mountain."

There is a surprise in the outcome.

A Reader Says

Stan and Judy should take the artifacts to a museum. The things they found are really neat and lots of people would enjoy seeing them.

How did you feel about the story?

After You Read

Thinking About What You Read

1. Why do you think Judy was more interested in the letter than in the German stamp?
2. How do you know that Judy and Stan are adventurous?
3. Why do you think the clue "Where the bear went over the mountain" was a good clue?
4. Suppose Judy and Stan had not found anything in the cave. Do you think they would still enjoy being on the mountain?

Thinking About How You Read

How did knowing that mystery stories have clues help you understand the story?

Sharing and Listening

Do you think Judy and Stan should keep the treasure, or do you think that the treasure should go to a museum? Share your opinion with your classmates. Give reasons for your answer. Listen carefully to the opinions of your classmates.

Writing

Imagine that you had hidden a treasure that you wanted a friend to find. Write a short letter to your friend that includes a riddle or a clue that tells where the treasure is.

It can be hard to find something that's been carefully hidden. Especially when you don't know what you're looking for! Juan and Elena have one clue to help them discover the Mystery of Corbin Lodge.

THE MYSTERY OF CORBIN LODGE

by Christine E. Scott

Elena sat up in bed suddenly; something strange had wakened her. She looked out the window beside her and saw the front yard below and a narrow strip of white sand by the lake. Everything was still in the moonlight.

Elena could hear the lake water lapping against the boats. Then there was another sound, a soft, crunching sound—like footsteps on sand.

The door behind her opened with a noisy squeak and Elena jumped. It was Juan. "Did you hear something?"

Elena nodded, and they peered out the window together. For a moment they saw a man walking along the water's edge; then he disappeared.

"He went toward the old Corbin Lodge!" Juan whispered.

Elena and her brother, Juan, had come to spend a few weeks at Stone Lake with Aunt Celia and Uncle Tomás. Around the bend in Stone Lake was an old weather-beaten two-story inn. They'd ask Uncle Tomás about it at the breakfast table.

The next morning, Juan and Elena talked excitedly about the man they'd seen the night before.

"Who do you think it was?" Elena asked.

"I don't know, but it's strange," said Uncle Tomás. "You'd better not go near Corbin Lodge; it hasn't been used for ten years."

"It's been empty since then?" Juan asked.

"As far as we know. Mrs. Corbin is the only one left of that family, and she now lives over by the store. Thaddeus Corbin was her husband's uncle."

"Thaddeus Corbin was strange," added Aunt Celia, "because he made up riddles all the time. He even left a riddle in his will about the lodge."

"It's said that after his death someone went into the lodge and never came out," said Uncle Tomás. "I know something's strange, because all the doors are locked from the inside, and people have heard closing doors and a clanging bell."

"Mrs. Corbin desperately needs money," Aunt Celia said. "If she can't sell the lodge soon, she may have to give up her home here. But she won't sell the lodge until the riddle's solved, because she thinks old Thaddeus hid something valuable there."

"Maybe it's a treasure!" Juan said. "What's the riddle he left in his will?"

"I'm going to see Mrs. Corbin tomorrow. Come along and we'll ask her," said Aunt Celia.

The next afternoon Aunt Celia, Juan, and Elena sat in Mrs. Corbin's living room.

"Elena and Juan have been hearing about the riddle in your uncle's will," Aunt Celia said. "Do you know any more about it?"

Mrs. Corbin sighed and said, "I've desperately tried to figure it out, but Uncle Thaddeus sure has me puzzled."

She went over to a desk, got out a tin box, and read from a small piece of paper:

> Look carefully where flowers entwine,
> And golden treasures you may find.

"There was a small flower garden back of the lodge," said Mrs. Corbin, "but it's been searched and dug up a dozen times."

"Could we look around?" Juan asked.

"Look all you want, outside or inside the lodge, but just be careful!"

It was early the next afternoon when they began their search, and they started in the garden.

"'Where flowers entwine.' There's a vine of flowers on that gate, so let's start there," Juan said.

After searching for more than an hour, they decided to dig a hole.

After they had dug for an hour, Elena asked, "Do you suppose, Juan, the answer to the riddle is *inside* the lodge, not outside?"

They went up to the back porch and Elena tried to open the doors. "The doors are locked from the inside," she said.

They found an unlocked window, climbed in, and tiptoed through the empty rooms and up the creaking stairs.

At the top of the stairs there was a narrow hallway with rooms on each side. As they started down the hall, they heard a door close downstairs.

"A closing door!" they both gasped.

They went into the last room at the end of the hall and sensed something different. "Look! This room has wallpaper on the walls, and it looks like roses on the paper," said Elena. "Hey, roses are flowers! And look at this seam in the wallpaper where the flowers entwine!"

59

They put their fingers along the seam, and then Juan pulled the paper away to reveal a small wooden door. He opened it and pulled out a tin box matching Mrs. Corbin's.

Then there were footsteps outside the door, and in the doorway stood a tall dark figure—the man by the lake!

"I'll take that box!" the man said as he took a step forward and snatched the box from Juan's hand. "I figured a couple of smart kids might find it," he said. "Now come with me and be quiet."

He ordered them to walk in front of him, and all the way down the stairs Juan was trying desperately to think of something he could do.

Downstairs the man said, "Now don't try anything; hold hands and go into the garden."

The garden! Juan's heart leaped and he pressed Elena's hand, hoping she understood. It might be their only chance!

The man walked close behind them. In the growing darkness, and with his mind on his captives, he did not see the hole they had dug. Just as they approached it, Juan jerked Elena's arm, and they leaped to the side. The man took a step forward and stumbled into the hole!

"Run, Elena!" Juan shouted, as the man grabbed for Juan.

Then a big voice boomed, "Oh, no you don't!" It was Uncle Tomás, who grasped the man's coat collar tightly.

"Are you okay?" asked Uncle Tomás.

"Sure," Juan grinned.

"This is Sam Rogers, who used to work for Thaddeus Corbin. He must have been living in the lodge until he could find the valuable treasure."

After Sam was delivered to the sheriff, they went to get Aunt Celia; then they rushed to Mrs. Corbin's house.

"You found it in the lodge? Where was it?" asked Mrs. Corbin, as Juan gave her the box.

After Juan and Elena excitedly told the whole story, Mrs. Corbin lifted the lid off the box.

"Gold coins!" Juan exclaimed. "I'll bet they're valuable ones!"

"So this was Uncle Thaddeus's 'golden treasure,'" Mrs. Corbin said as she looked at Elena and Juan. "Thanks to you, I can stay here. Everyone must stay for supper!"

What an evening it was! As they ate the delicious meal, Juan and Elena felt they had never been so happy or so hungry before.

A Reader Says

After Mrs. Corbin got the coins, I think she should have given Juan and Elena a reward.

How did you feel about the story?

After You Read

Thinking About What You Read

1. What do you think is mysterious about Corbin Lodge?

2. Why do you think Elena suggested she and Juan look inside the lodge for an answer to the riddle?

3. How do you know that Elena and Juan are two smart kids?

4. Juan and Elena were happy with their discovery even though they did not receive a reward. Why do you think this is so?

Thinking About How You Read

How did knowing that this story is a mystery help you understand it?

Sharing and Listening

Do you think Juan and Elena should have received a reward for finding the treasure? Why or why not? Share your opinion with your classmates. Listen carefully to their opinions.

Writing

Pretend you are a news reporter sent to cover the mystery of Corbin Lodge. Write a newspaper article telling about Juan and Elena's discovery of the treasure.

When Peter and Judy find a game in the park, they don't realize the discovery they've made.

Jumanji

◆

by Chris Van Allsburg

"Now remember," Mother said, "your father and I are bringing some guests by after the opera, so please keep the house neat."

"Quite so," added Father, tucking his scarf inside his coat.

Mother peered into the hall mirror and carefully pinned her hat in place, then knelt and kissed both children good-bye.

When the front door closed, Judy and Peter giggled with delight. They took all the toys out of their toy chest and made a terrible mess. But their laughter slowly turned to silence till finally Peter slouched into a chair.

"You know what?" he said. "I'm really bored."

"Me too," sighed Judy. "Why don't we go outside and play?" Peter agreed, so they set off across the street to the park. It was cold for November.

The children could see their breath like steam.
They rolled in the leaves and when Judy tried to
stuff some leaves down Peter's sweater he jumped
up and ran behind a tree. When his sister caught
up with him, he was kneeling at the foot of the
tree, looking at a long thin box.

"What's that?" Judy asked.

"It's a game," said Peter, handing her the box.

"'JUMANJI,'" Judy read from the box, "'A JUNGLE ADVENTURE GAME.'"

"Look," said Peter, pointing to a note taped to the bottom of the box. In a childlike handwriting were the words "Free game, fun for some but not for all. P.S. Read instructions carefully."

"Want to take it home?" Judy asked.

"Not really," said Peter. "I'm sure somebody left it here because it's so boring."

"Oh, come on," protested Judy. "Let's give it a try. Race you home!" And off she ran with Peter at her heels.

At home, the children spread the game out on a card table. It looked very much like the games they already had. There was a board that unfolded, revealing a path of colored squares. The squares had messages written on them. The path started in the deepest jungle and ended up in Jumanji, a city of golden buildings and towers. Peter began to shake the dice and play with the other pieces that were in the box.

"Put those down and listen," said Judy. "I'm going to read the instructions: 'Jumanji, a young people's jungle adventure especially designed for the bored and restless.

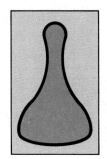

"'A. Player selects piece and places it in deepest jungle. B. Player rolls dice and moves piece along path through the dangers of the jungle. C. First player to reach Jumanji and yell the city's name aloud is the winner.'"

"Is that all?" asked Peter, sounding disappointed.

"No," said Judy, "there's one more thing, and this is in capital letters: 'D. VERY IMPORTANT: ONCE A GAME OF JUMANJI IS STARTED IT WILL NOT BE OVER UNTIL ONE PLAYER REACHES THE GOLDEN CITY.'"

"Oh, big deal," said Peter, who gave a bored
yawn.
"Here," said Judy, handing her brother the dice,
"you go first."
Peter casually dropped the dice from his hand.
"Seven," said Judy.

Peter moved his piece to the seventh square.

"'Lion attacks, move back two spaces,'" read Judy.

"Gosh, how exciting," said Peter, in a very unexcited voice. As he reached for his piece he looked up at his sister. She had a look of absolute horror on her face.

"Peter," she whispered, "turn around very, very slowly."

The boy turned in his chair. He couldn't believe his eyes. Lying on the piano was a lion, staring at Peter and licking his lips.

The lion roared so loud it knocked Peter right off his chair. The big cat jumped to the floor. Peter was up on his feet, running through the house with the lion a whisker's length behind. He ran upstairs and dove under a bed. The lion tried to squeeze under, but got his head stuck. Peter scrambled out, ran from the bedroom, and slammed the door behind him. He stood in the hall with Judy, gasping for breath.

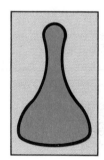

"I don't think," said Peter in between gasps of air, "that I want . . . to play . . . this game . . . anymore."

"But we have to," said Judy as she helped Peter back downstairs. "I'm sure that's what the instructions mean. That lion won't go away until one of us wins the game."

Peter stood next to the card table. "Can't we just call the zoo and have him taken away?" From upstairs came the sounds of growling and clawing at the bedroom door. "Or maybe we could wait till Father comes home."

"No one would come from the zoo because they wouldn't believe us," said Judy. "And you know how upset Mother would be if there was a lion in the bedroom. We started this game and now we have to finish it."

Peter looked down at the game board. What if Judy rolled a seven? Then there'd be two lions. For an instant Peter thought he was going to cry. Then he sat firmly in his chair and said, "Let's play."

Judy picked up the dice, rolled an eight, and moved her piece. "'Monkeys steal food, miss one turn,'" she read.

From the kitchen came the sounds of banging pots and falling jars. The children ran in to see a dozen monkeys tearing the room apart.

"Oh boy," said Peter, "this would upset Mother even more than the lion."

"Quick," said Judy, "back to the game."

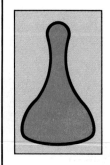

Peter took his turn. Thank heavens, he landed on a blank space. He rolled again. "'Monsoon season begins, lose one turn.'"

Little raindrops began to fall in the living room. Then a roll of thunder shook the walls and scared the monkeys out of the kitchen. The rain began to fall in buckets as Judy took the dice.

"'Guide gets lost, lose one turn.'" The rain suddenly stopped. The children turned to see a man hunched over a map.

"Oh dear, I say, spot of bad luck now," he mumbled. "Perhaps a left turn here then . . . No, no, . . . a right turn here . . . Yes, absolutely, I think, a right turn . . . or maybe . . ."

"Excuse me," said Judy, but the guide just
ignored her.

". . . around here, then over . . . No,
no . . . over here and around this . . . Yes,
good . . . but then . . . Hm . . ."

Judy shrugged her shoulders and handed the
dice to Peter.

"... four, five, six," he counted. "'Bitten by tsetse fly, contract sleeping sickness, lose one turn.'"

Judy heard a faint buzzing noise and watched a small insect land on Peter's nose. Peter lifted his hand to brush the bug away, but then stopped, gave a tremendous yawn, and fell sound asleep, his head on the table.

"Peter, Peter, wake up!" cried Judy. But it was no use. She grabbed the dice and moved to a blank. She rolled again and waited in amazement. "'Rhinoceros stampede, go back two spaces.'"

As fast as he had fallen asleep, Peter awoke. Together they listened to a rumble in the hallway. It grew louder and louder. Suddenly a herd of rhinos charged through the living room and into the dining room, crushing all the furniture in their path. Peter and Judy covered their ears as sounds of splintering wood and breaking china filled the house.

Peter gave the dice a quick tumble. "'Python sneaks into camp, go back one space.'"

Judy shrieked and jumped up on her chair.

"Over the fireplace," said Peter. Judy sat down again, nervously eyeing the eight-foot snake that was wrapping itself around the mantel clock. The guide looked up from his map, took one look at the snake, and moved to the far corner of the room, joining the monkeys on the couch.

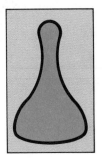

Judy took her turn and landed on a blank space. Her brother took the dice and rolled a three.

"Oh, no," he moaned. "'Volcano erupts, go back three spaces.'" The room became warm and started to shake a little. Molten lava poured from the fireplace opening. It hit the water on the floor and the room filled with steam. Judy rolled the dice and moved ahead.

"'Discover shortcut, roll again.' Oh dear!" she cried. Judy saw the snake unwrapping himself from the clock.

"If you roll a twelve you can get out of the jungle," said Peter.

"Please, please," Judy begged as she shook the dice. The snake was wriggling his way to the floor. She dropped the dice from her hand. One six, then another. Judy grabbed her piece and slammed it to the board. "JUMANJI," she yelled, as loud as she could.

The steam in the room became thicker and thicker. Judy could not even see Peter across the table. Then, as if all the doors and windows had been opened, a cool breeze cleared the steam from the room. Everything was just as it had been before the game. No monkeys, no guide, no water, no broken furniture, no snake, no lion roaring upstairs, no rhinos. Without saying a word to each other, Peter and Judy threw the game into its box. They bolted out the door, ran across the street to the park, and dropped the game under a tree. Back home, they quickly put all their toys away. But both children were too excited to sit quietly, so Peter took out a picture puzzle. As they fit the pieces together, their excitement slowly turned to relief, and then exhaustion. With the puzzle half done Peter and Judy fell sound asleep on the sofa.

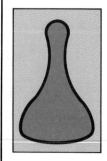

"Wake up, dears," Mother's voice called.

Judy opened her eyes. Mother and Father had returned and their guests were arriving. Judy gave Peter a nudge to wake him. Yawning and stretching, they got to their feet.

Mother introduced them to some of the guests, then asked, "Did you have an exciting afternoon?"

"Oh yes," said Peter. "We had a flood, a stampede, a volcano, I got sleeping sickness, and—" Peter was interrupted by the adults' laughter.

"Well," said Mother, "I think you both got sleeping sickness. Why don't you go upstairs and put your pajamas on? Then you can finish your puzzle and have some dinner."

When Peter and Judy came back downstairs they found that Father had moved the puzzle into the den. While the children were working on it, one of the guests, Mrs. Budwing, brought them a tray of food.

"Such a hard puzzle," she said to the children. "Daniel and Walter are always starting puzzles and never finishing them." Daniel and Walter were Mrs. Budwing's sons. "They never read instructions either. Oh well," said Mrs. Budwing, turning to rejoin the guests, "I guess they'll learn."

Both children answered, "I hope so," but they weren't looking at Mrs. Budwing. They were looking out the window. Two boys were running through the park. It was Danny and Walter Budwing, and Danny had a long thin box under his arm.

A Reader Says

Peter and Judy should have kept JUMANJI. Once they relax and think about it, they might decide to play it again someday.

How did you feel about the story?

75

About the Author

Chris Van Allsburg

Chris Van Allsburg says that writing and making picture books is exciting. Between the covers of each book he can create a small world. It can show fantastic things in real-life places. This makes his stories and pictures seem like something you might see in a dream.

He got the idea for *Jumanji* when he remembered how exciting he found board games as a child. So he started drawing Peter and Judy. They were playing a game named *Jumanji*.

Mr. Van Allsburg likes to make pictures of things that don't belong together. That's why he shows such things as a train or a rhinoceros herd in the childrens' living room. He draws his pictures with black crayon or pen. It is hard to make line drawings that are so sharp and exact. He uses both dark and light shapes to make things stand out and seem real. Some of his drawings hang in museums. His books, which include *Jumanji, The Garden of Abdul Gaszi, Ben's Dream* and *The Polar Express*, have won many awards.

More Books About Discoveries

Aesop's Fables
by Aesop, illustrated by Heidi Holder
Each of these famous fables tells an important story. Like the town mouse and the country mouse, the animals in these tales make discoveries about themselves and the world around them that teach helpful lessons about life.

Lights Around the Palm
by Mavis Jukes
Emma can do surprising things with her imagination. Even though she is young, she has a lot to teach others. The people and animals around her discover something new with Emma's help.

Stories Julian Tells
by Ann Cameron
Would you like to read more about Julian, his friends, and his family? This book will provide you with lots of stories about Julian and his adventures in growing up.

Surfboard to Peril
by Robert Quackenbush
Miss Mallard is a "ducktective" with a talent for solving mysteries. Hunt down clues with her in sunny Hawaii, and maybe you can guess the solution!

MAKING ALL THE
CONNECTIONS

Speaking and Listening

In this part of the book, you read about many kinds of discoveries. The characters in some of the stories discovered something about themselves. In other stories, the characters discovered the solutions to old puzzles. You read how the country mouse discovers that her life is the one she likes best. You read how a young boy discovers the world through the experiences he shares with his grandfather. You also read how Juan and Elena discover the solution to an old mystery, and how a strange game called *Jumanji* leads to amazing discoveries.

Discuss the stories you read with your classmates. You may want to look back at your Reader's Log. Speak clearly when you give your ideas. Listen carefully as others share their ideas with you. Here are some questions to help you talk about the unit.

1. How were the discoveries you read about in this unit alike? How were they different?

2. Think about your own life. What discoveries have you made? Are there others that you would like to make?

3. Talk about different kinds of discoveries. Which do you think are most important?

Discover a Favorite Story

In this part of the book, you have read about discoveries. Now, you are going to make a discovery of your own. You are going to discover something that has probably been in your mind for a long, long time. You are going to discover a story that was told to you when you were very young.

You have probably heard lots and lots of stories. Think about some of them. Which story would you like to hear told again? Which story do you remember well enough to tell others? Even if a story is one that everyone has heard, maybe the way you heard it was a little bit different. Maybe your storyteller used special words or different sound effects. Think about all of these things as you decide on the story that you are going to tell.

Here are some other things for you to think about:

◆ When did this story take place?
◆ Where did it take place?
◆ Who are the characters?
◆ What did the characters do?

Working Together to Tell a Story

Tell your story to a classmate. It will be your classmate's job to listen carefully to what you say. Your classmate will also pay attention to *how* you are saying it. Later, you will help your classmate in the same way.

If something in your story is hard to understand, your classmate should tell you. Then you can work together to straighten out the problem. When it is your turn to listen, you will do the same thing.

Here are some ideas about what you should listen for in your classmate's story. Can you think of anything else? Add it to the list.

- Did your classmate describe the characters so that you could almost see them?
- Did your classmate tell the events of the story in the order that they happened?
- Did your classmate remember to tell where and when the story takes place?

Once you have decided what you are going to say, it is time to think about how you are going to say it. Here are some ideas to think about. Add your own ideas to the list.

- Did you speak slowly and clearly enough for everyone to hear you?
- Did you look at your audience?
- Did you change your tone of voice as you spoke?
- Did you use sound effects and different voices for the characters?

Presenting Your Story

When you have practiced enough with your partner, it is time to share your story with the rest of the class. It is also time for you to listen to other stories. It is storytelling time! Make it a good time for you and your classmates.

You may want to sit in a circle to share your stories. Take turns being the storyteller. Listen quietly and carefully to each story. Think about how they are different and about how they are the same.

After each story has been told, ask questions about anything you did not understand. Share with your classmates what you thought about the story and the way it was told.

You can share your stories in other ways. Here are some suggestions. If you wish, you can add some suggestions of your own to the list.

Present your stories to another class: Vote on the stories that you like the best. Then, share them with another class. You can be like the traveling storytellers of long ago.

Tape record your stories: Record your stories to share with the whole school. You can ask the school librarian to set up a tape recorder in the school library where other students might enjoy listening to your favorite stories.

PART TWO

Changes

So many little flowers
Drop their tiny heads
But newer buds come to bloom
In their place instead.

from *Cycle*
by Langston Hughes

◆

Change is a part of everyone's life. Without it, we couldn't grow up. The people you'll meet in these stories are all facing important changes in their lives. As you read, think: What changes have helped *you* learn and grow?

83

Exploring Words About Changes

Starting with What You Know

Changes happen every day. What changes come to mind? The words in the box below tell about changes. Use these words and words of your own to answer the questions after the box.

blossom	fall	haircut
spring	grow	travel
learn	new friend	move

It gets colder when autumn turns to winter. What other things happen when the seasons change? Many children grow taller as they get older. What other kinds of changes occur as a child gets older? Some people like to change their surroundings. How might people change their surroundings?

Building a Word Map

The word map shows how some of the words in the box above go together. Think about words you can add to the map. Use words from the box and other words of your own.

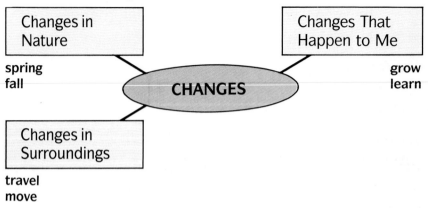

Changes in Nature
spring
fall

Changes That Happen to Me
grow
learn

CHANGES

Changes in Surroundings
travel
move

Finishing a Story

Look at the story below. The story tells about how a tree changes as the seasons change. Some words are missing. Think of the words you would use to finish the story. Use the words from the box and word map in this lesson for ideas. Complete the story.

It is spring in the forest. A small tree reaches its branches towards the sky. _____ begin to sprout from the tree and turn _____. In the branches, birds begin to _____ their nests.

In summer, the tree feels the warm rays of the _____. It feels _____ blowing through its branches. It feels the rain on its leaves. The tree grows _____.

Soon the _____ turns cold. The birds leave to fly south. The leaves turn a beautiful _____. They begin to _____.

Soon it will become colder. _____ will fall. The _____ season will come.

Share your story with your classmates. What words did you use to tell about the changes?

As You Read

In this part of the book, you will read about different kinds of changes. Keeping a Reader's Log will help you remember important thoughts, ideas, and words. As you read, make notes in your log. You could begin your Reader's Log with the word map. Add new words to the map as you find them.

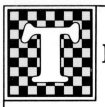

THEME SETTER

Moving out West from New York City is a hard change to make. Especially when your best friend tells you Gila monsters meet you at the airport. Could Seymour be right?

Gila Monsters
Meet You at the Airport

◆

by Marjorie Weinman Sharmat

I live at 165 East 95th Street, New York City, and I'm going to stay here forever.

My mother and father are moving. Out West. They say I have to go, too. They say I can't stay here forever.

Out West nobody plays baseball because they're too busy chasing buffaloes. And there's cactus everywhere you look. But if you don't look, you have to stand up just as soon as you sit down.

Out West it takes fifteen minutes just to say hello. Like this: H-O-W-W-W-D-Y, P-A-A-A-R-D-N-E-R.

Out West I'll look silly all the time. I'll have to wear chaps and spurs and a bandanna and a hat so big that nobody can find me underneath it. I'll have to ride a horse to school and I don't know how.

My best friend is Seymour, and we like to eat salami sandwiches together. Out West I probably won't have any friends, but if I do, they'll be named Tex or Slim, and we'll eat chili and beans for breakfast. And lunch. And dinner.

Seymour says there are Gila[1] monsters and horned toads out West, and I read it in a book so I know it's so. But Seymour says they meet you at the airport.

We're here. Out West. I don't know what a Gila monster or horned toad looks like, but I don't think I see any at the airport.

I see a boy in a cowboy hat. He looks like Seymour, but I know his name is Tex. "Hi," I say.

"Hi," he says. "I'm moving East."

"Great!" I say.

[1](hē′ lə)

"*Great?*" he says. "What's so great about it? Don't you know that the streets are full of gangsters? They all wear flowers in their lapels so they look honest, but they zoom around in big cars with screeching brakes. You have to jump out of their way.

"In the East it snows and blows all the time, except for five minutes when it's spring and summer. And you have to live on the 50th floor. Airplanes fly through your bedroom, and you've got to duck fast.

"They ran out of extra space in the East a long time ago. It's so crowded people sit on top of each other when they ride to work. And alligators live in the sewers. I read it in a book so I know it's so."

Then the mother and father of the boy who looks like Seymour but isn't grab his hand, and he goes off. "Sometimes the alligators get out," he yells to me. "And they wait for you at the airport."

It's warm, but there's a nice breeze. We're in a taxi riding to our new house.

No horses yet. I don't see any buffalo stampedes either. I see a restaurant just like the one in my old neighborhood. I see some kids playing baseball. I see a horse. Hey, that's a great-looking horse! I'm going to ask my mother and father for one like it.

Here's our house. Some kids are riding their bikes in front of it. I hope one of them is named Slim.

Tomorrow I'm writing a long letter to Seymour. I'll tell him I'm sending it by pony express. Seymour will believe me. Back East they don't know much about us Westerners.

Thinking About the Theme

1. What changes about moving do you think would be the most difficult?

2. Imagine that in five years the boy returns East for a visit. How do you think he will react to being back in the city?

COMPREHENSION
BUILDER

for **Words in Our Hands** and **The Rooster Who Understood Japanese**

Making a Summary

Starting with What You Know

The cartoon has only four parts. It shows the important parts of a story you have read. What is the story?

Thinking About Making a Summary

You can write a summary to help you remember the important parts of a story. Your summary will tell the name of the story and what the story is about. It will tell who the main characters are and what they did. It will tell how the story ends.

Read the summary at the top of the next page. One thing in the summary is not as important as the other things. What is it?

The Mystery of Corbin Lodge is about a brother and sister who look for a hidden treasure. Juan and Elena are the main characters. In the story, a man's coat collar was grabbed. The children get involved in a mystery surrounding a house. Finally, they find the treasure and solve the mystery at the same time. The story ends when the house's owner thanks them for their help.

Remember that a summary tells only the important things that happen. In the summary above, the man's collar being grabbed is not important.

Practice

On another piece of paper, finish the summary for *Gila Monsters Meet You at the Airport*.

Gila Monsters Meet You at the Airport is about _____.
The main character is _____. In the story, he _____.
The story ends when _____.

As You Read

Making a summary helps you remember the important things about a story. Ask yourself these questions as you read:
- What is the story about?
- Who are the main characters?
- What are the important things that happen?
- How does the story end?

Apply what you know about making a summary as you read the two selections that follow. Use the side notes to help you.

Moving to a new town is always a big change.
Moving is a special problem for Michael's family
because his parents are deaf.

WORDS
IN OUR HANDS

by Ada B. Litchfield

My name is Michael Turner, and I am nine years old. I have two sisters, Gina and Diane, a dog named Polly, and two parents who cannot hear me when I talk.

They never have heard me, because my mom and dad were born deaf.

My parents never heard any sounds at all when they were babies. Some people think a person who can't hear can't learn to talk, but that's not true.

Michael and his family are the main characters.

My mom and dad went to a school for deaf kids when they were growing up—that's where they were taught to talk. They learned by placing their fingers on their teacher's throat and feeling how words *felt* in her voice box as she said them. They learned how words *looked* by watching her lips and face as she spoke. It's hard to learn to say words that way, but my parents did.

Sometimes my mother and father can understand what people are saying by reading their lips. That's another thing my parents learned at their school—lip reading.

How we move our bodies and what our faces look like when we talk help our parents read our lips, but most of the time we talk to them with our hands as well as our mouths. My Grandma Ellis says we have words in our hands.

Think about the title of the story. Now you know what it means.

Gina, Diane, and I are learning new signs all the time. My mother and father learned sign language when they were little. And they taught us signs when we were babies, just as hearing parents teach their children words. Our grandparents, friends, and neighbors helped us learn to talk.

My parents have some neat things to help them. In our house, when the telephone or doorbell rings, flashing lights come on. We have a TTY—a teletypewriter—attached to our phone. The teletypewriter spells out messages on tape, and then my parents can type messages back.

Of course, the person calling us has to have a teletypewriter, and not very many people do. That means that many times we kids have to talk on the phone for our parents. And sometimes we have to talk to people who come to the door.

When we were babies, my mother or father checked on us very often to be sure we were all right. They took turns at night. They also used a cry alarm, which is a microphone hooked up to a light. When we cried, a light would flash in our parents' bedroom or in the kitchen or living room.

When Diane was little, Gina and I helped take care of her. We would hear when she cried and tell my mom or dad.

Some deaf people have a hearing ear dog to help them, and we have Polly. Polly hasn't been taught hand signals the way real hearing ear dogs have, but she is learning to do many things a hearing ear dog does.

Polly gets my mother up by tugging at her blankets if her flashing-light alarm doesn't wake her. She runs back and forth to let my mom and dad know that someone is at the door. She makes a big fuss if a flashing-light alarm goes off or if a pan is boiling over on the stove.

Just because my parents are deaf doesn't mean we don't do things other families do. My mom and dad go to programs at school. We have friends over for dinner and to stay all night. We go on picnics, and sometimes we drive to the city to the Science Museum.

We are a happy family—at least we were until about six months ago. Then the publishing company where my father has always worked moved to a new town, one hundred miles away.

My father is an editor of a magazine about farming. Nobody in the family wanted to move, but my father loves his job so, of course, he wanted to move with his company.

We bought a new house with a big yard that everybody liked, but it took time to get used to our new town. Before, my mom had always done all the shopping and banking for our family. Now she felt a little strange going into a store where the people didn't know her, so very often she wanted Gina or me to go with her.

In our old town, everybody was friendly and knew our family. Nobody stared when they saw us talking with our hands. But in the new town, people did stare, and sometimes Gina and I felt embarrassed.

Gina and I didn't want to feel that way, and we understood how shy our parents felt. We knew Mom missed her art class. We knew they both missed their old friends and were as lonesome and homesick as we were!

One day Gina's favorite teacher gave her a note to take home. It was an invitation for our family to go to a performance of the National Theatre of the Deaf.

At first, I didn't want to give the invitation to my parents. I didn't want them to go because I didn't want people to make fun of them or feel sorry for Gina and me.

But Gina said they should go. She said that the play would be in sign language, and who would understand it better than our parents? I knew she was right, and besides, Mom and Dad needed to go out and meet new people.

This is an important new change for the family. Predict what might happen.

The family has a problem getting used to the new town.

Still, I was worried about what might happen. The night of the play, all sorts of questions were popping into my mind as I dragged myself up the steps into the hall.

The theater was filled with people. Just inside the door, my mother signed to me. "Where will we sit?"

To our surprise, a man stood up and signed, "There are five seats over here."

We couldn't believe it—he was talking in sign language!

All around us, people were laughing and talking. They seemed so friendly. Many of them were talking with their hands, and they didn't seem to care who was watching.

Michael was surprised. An important thing happened.

Before the play started, we learned from our program that some of the actors were deaf and some could hear. The hearing actors and some of the deaf actors would speak in the play. All of the actors would sign, sometimes for themselves and sometimes for each other, and sometimes they would all sign together. Everyone in the audience would be able to understand what was going on.

The play we saw was called *The Wooden Boy*, and it was about Pinocchio, a puppet who wanted to be a real boy.

After the play, we went backstage to meet the actors. The deaf performers talked with people who knew sign language. The hearing actors helped the other people understand what was being said.

I was proud of my parents. They were smiling, and their fingers were flying as fast as anyone's. For the first time in many months, they seemed to feel at home.

This is not an important fact.

98

Then we had another surprise when Gina's teacher came over to us. She talked very slowly and carefully so my mother could read her lips; then she signed with her hands!

Gina was excited, because her favorite teacher who wasn't deaf, had words in her hands, too. Gina was learning something she didn't know before; we all were. We were learning there were many friendly people in our new town who could talk with our parents. I decided this place wasn't going to be so bad after all.

People in the town helped the family solve its problem.

A Reader Says

I bet it's fun to have a teletypewriter. If everyone had one, deaf people could call anywhere.

How did you feel about the story?

After You Read

Thinking About What You Read

1. Why do you think Grandma Ellis says that the children have words in their hands?
2. Why do you think other people helped the children learn to talk?
3. How do you know Michael felt uncomfortable in the new town?
4. Why do you think going to a performance of The National Theatre of the Deaf was an important event for the family?

Thinking About How You Read

How did making a summary help you find the important details in this story?

Sharing and Listening

Do you think that most people should learn sign language? Why or why not? Explain your ideas, then listen carefully as your classmates give their ideas.

Writing

Suppose you were to move to a new town one hundred miles away. Write a letter to a friend. Tell your friend about your new home and how you feel about the change.

PEOPLE

Some people talk and talk
and never say a thing.
Some people look at you
and birds begin to sing.

Some people laugh and laugh
and yet you want to cry.
Some people touch your hand
and music fills the sky.

Charlotte Zolotow

101

Some changes seem terrible at first. Mrs. Kitamura can't believe she must give up the pet rooster she loves. Could it be a change for the better?

THE ROOSTER WHO UNDERSTOOD JAPANESE

by Yoshiko Uchida

"Mrs. K.!" Miyo called. "I'm here!"

Every afternoon when Miyo came home from school, where she was in the third grade, she went to the home of her neighbor, Mrs. Kitamura, whom she called "Mrs. K."

This was because Miyo's mother was a doctor at University Hospital and didn't get home until supper time.

It was a fine arrangement all around because Mrs. Kitamura was a widow, and she enjoyed Miyo's company. Not that she was lonely. She had a basset hound named Jefferson, a ten-year-old parrot named Hamilton, a coal black cat named Leonardo, and a pet rooster named Mr. Lincoln. She talked to all of them in Japanese. She also talked to the onions and potatoes she'd planted in her front yard instead of a lawn, coaxing them to grow plump and delicious.

102

About the time Miyo came home from school, Mrs. K. was usually outside talking to her potatoes and onions, but today Mrs. K. was nowhere to be seen. She wasn't out front, and she wasn't in back talking to any of her animals either.

Her dog, Jefferson, stretched sleepily and came to greet Miyo as she opened the gate to the backyard.

"Hello, Jefferson Kitamura," Miyo said. "Where's Mrs. K.?"

Jefferson wagged his tail and sniffed at Miyo. Then he went back to his special spot at the foot of the willow tree, and curled up to get on with his afternoon nap.

Miyo stopped next to see Mr. Lincoln. He was strutting about in his pen making roosterlike sounds and looking very intelligent and dignified.

Mrs. K. had told Miyo that he understood every word she said to him, whether she spoke in English or Japanese.

"Mrs. Kitamura, *doko*?" Miyo said, asking Mr. Lincoln where she was.

He cocked his head, looked at her with his small bright eyes, and uttered a squawking sound.

Miyo shrugged. Maybe Mr. Lincoln did understand Japanese, but it certainly didn't do any good if she couldn't understand what he said back to her.

"Never mind," she said. "I'll find her." And she hurried toward the brown shingled house covered with ivy that hung over it like droopy hair. The back door was unlatched, and Miyo walked in.

"Mrs. K., I'm here," she called once more.

Miyo went into the dining room and found Mrs. K. sitting at the big oval table. She was making herself a cup of ceremonial Japanese tea, whipping up the special powdered green tea in a beautiful tea bowl with a small bamboo whisk.

"*Mah*!" Mrs. K. said, looking startled. "I was so busy with my thoughts, I didn't even hear you come in."

Miyo looked at the green froth of tea in the tea bowl, knowing it was strong and bitter. "Is that our afternoon tea?" she asked, trying not to look too disappointed.

"No, no, not yours," Mrs. K. answered quickly. "Just mine. I made it to calm myself." She turned the bowl around carefully and drank it in the proper three and a half sips. "There," she sighed.

"Are you calm now?"

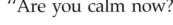

Mrs. K. shook her head. "Not really. Actually, not at all. As a matter of fact, I am most upset."

Miyo wondered now why Mrs. K. was so upset. Usually she was full of fun, but today she scarcely smiled at Miyo.

Mrs. Kitamura stood up and started toward the kitchen, and Leonardo appeared from beneath her chair to follow close behind.

"I've been upset since seven o'clock this morning," she explained suddenly.

"Why?" Miyo asked, gratefully accepting a glass of milk. "Did you get out of the wrong side of bed?"

That was what her mother sometimes asked when Miyo was grumpy. But that wasn't Mrs. K.'s trouble at all.

"It's not me. It's my new neighbor, Mr. Wickett. He told me that if Mr. Lincoln didn't stop waking him up by crowing at six in the morning, he was going to report me to the police for disturbing the peace! What am I going to do?" Mrs. K. asked, as though Miyo were the wise old woman in the Japanese tale who could answer any puzzling question put to her. "I can't go out and tell Mr. Lincoln he is not to crow anymore. You and your mama have never complained."

Miyo didn't say that they were already up at six o'clock anyway. She wondered what she could say to make Mrs. K. feel better, and finally she said, "I'll ask my mother. She'll know what to do."

"Don't worry, Mama will think of something," Miyo said as she left Mrs. Kitamura's house.

When Miyo got home, Mother was starting supper. "Hi sweetie," she called. "How was Mrs. K.?"

"She was worried," Miyo answered as she set the table. "She has to make Mr. Lincoln stop crowing."

"Whatever for?"

Miyo quickly told Mother about Mr. Wickett. "Mr. Lincoln doesn't hurt anybody."

But Mother said, "Well, I can see Mr. Wickett's side too. If I could sleep late, I'm not so sure I'd like having a rooster wake me at six o'clock. "Besides," she added, "our town is growing, and we're in the city limits now. Maybe Mrs. K. will just have to give Mr. Lincoln away."

Miyo didn't even want to think of such a thing. "But he's not just any old rooster," she objected.

Mother nodded sympathetically. "I know," she said. "Well, maybe we can think of something."

But nobody could. Not Mother, not Miyo, nor Mrs. K.

That first night Mrs. K. brought Mr. Lincoln inside the house and put him into a big cardboard carton in her bedroom.

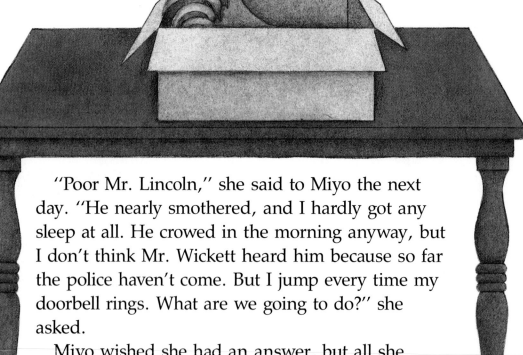

"Poor Mr. Lincoln," she said to Miyo the next day. "He nearly smothered, and I hardly got any sleep at all. He crowed in the morning anyway, but I don't think Mr. Wickett heard him because so far the police haven't come. But I jump every time my doorbell rings. What are we going to do?" she asked.

Miyo wished she had an answer, but all she could say was, "Mama and I are both thinking hard."

But Mother was so tired at the end of a long day at the hospital that she just couldn't find any good ideas. She did say, however, that keeping Mr. Lincoln inside a carton was not the answer.

And Mrs. K. certainly found out it wasn't. On the second night she brought him inside, Mr. Lincoln poked his way right out of the carton and walked all over her house. He scratched the floors and pecked at her sofa and got into a fight with Leonardo, the cat.

"I suppose I will have to give Mr. Lincoln away," Mrs. K. murmured sadly. "But I can't give him to just anybody. It has to be someone who will love him and not turn him into fricassee or stew."

Miyo thought and thought until her jaws ached. How in the world could they find just the right person to take Mr. Lincoln? Then, suddenly, she had an idea.

"I know," she said brightly. "I'll put an ad in our class magazine."

Mrs. K. thought about it. "Well," she said slowly. "I suppose it won't do any harm."

Miyo's class magazine was almost ready to be mimeographed for the month of October. She made her ad very special. She wrote,

"WANTED: NICE HOME FOR FRIENDLY, INTELLIGENT, DIGNIFIED ROOSTER. P.S. HE UNDERSTANDS JAPANESE." Then she added, "PLEASE HURRY! URGENT!"

The magazine came out on September 30. That very afternoon, a policeman rang the doorbell of Mrs. K.'s shaggy ivy-covered house.

"I've a complaint, Ma'm," he said, "about a rooster?" He seemed to think there might have been some mistake.

Mrs. K. sighed. "Come inside, officer," she said. "I've been expecting you."

Officer McArdle was tired and his feet hurt. "Thank you," he said, and he came inside.

"*Dozo*," she said, "please have some tea." She took off her apron and smoothed down her frizzy gray hair. Then she told him all about her troubles with Mr. Lincoln.

He looked sympathetic, but he said, "You're breaking a city law by having a rooster in your yard. You really should be fined, you know."

Mrs. K. was astonished. "Even if I am only barely inside the city limits?"

Officer McArdle nodded. "I'm afraid so. I'll give you two more days to get rid of your rooster. Mr. Wickett says you're disturbing the peace."

Then he thanked her for the tea and he was gone.

Miyo was proud of the ad in her class magazine, but no one seemed at all interested in Mr. Lincoln. Instead, several people told her how much they liked her feature story about Mr. Botts, the school custodian, who was retiring.

She had written, "Say good-bye to the best custodian Hawthorn School ever had. Mr. Botts is retiring because he is getting tired. At the age of sixty-five, who wouldn't? He and Mrs. Botts are going to Far Creek. He is going to eat a lot and sleep a lot and maybe go fishing. So, so long, Mr. Botts. And good luck!"

On her way home, Miyo ran into Mr. Botts himself. He told her it was the first time in his life that anyone had written a story about him.

When he got home that night, he took off his shoes, sat in his favorite chair, and read the magazine from cover to cover. At the bottom of page twenty, he saw Miyo's ad.

"Tami," he said to Mrs. Botts, who happened to be Japanese, "how would you like to have a rooster? One that understands Japanese."

Mrs. Botts thought that Mr. Botts had had too much excitement, what with his retirement party at school and all. But he kept right on talking.

"When we move to Far Creek, didn't you say you were going to grow vegetables and raise chickens?"

Mrs. Botts remembered having said something like that. "Yes, I guess I did."

"Then we might as well have a rooster that's friendly and dignified," Mr. Botts said, and he went right to the telephone to call Miyo.

"I'll take that rooster you want to find a home for," he said. "My wife could talk to it in Japanese too."

Miyo couldn't believe it. Someone had actually read her ad and that someone was Mr. Botts. As soon as she told Mother, she ran right over to tell Mrs. K. the good news.

When Miyo told Mrs. K. that Mr. Lincoln would have a nice half-Japanese home in Far Creek with Mr. and Mrs. Botts, Mrs. K. gave Miyo such a hug she almost squeezed the breath out of her.

"Hooray! *Banzai!*" Mrs. K. said happily. "Tomorrow we will have a party to celebrate. I shall invite you and your mama, and Mr. and Mrs. Botts." And because Mrs. K. felt so relieved and happy, she even decided to invite Mr. Wickett.

Mr. Wickett was a little embarrassed to come to Mrs. K.'s party, but he was too lonely to say no. He came and said, "I'm sorry I caused such a commotion."

But Mrs. K. told him he needn't be sorry. "Life needs a little stirring up now and then," she admitted. "Besides," she added, "now both Mr. Lincoln and I have found new friends."

"You come on out to visit us and your rooster any time you like," Mr. Botts said.

When the party was over, Mr. Botts carried Mr. Lincoln in a crate to his station wagon. Mr. Lincoln gave a polite squawk of farewell and Mrs. K. promised she would come visit him soon.

"Good-bye, Mr. Lincoln. Good-bye, Mr. and Mrs. Botts," Miyo called.

"I hope we'll see each other again soon," Mr. Wickett said to Mrs. K.

"Good night, Mr. Wickett," she answered. "I'm sure we will."

Miyo and her mother thanked Mrs. K. for the nice party and went home, leaving her to say good night to her potatoes and onions before going inside.

"Do you think she'll miss Mr. Lincoln a lot?" Miyo asked.

"She will for a while," Mother answered, "but now she has a new friend and neighbor to talk to."

Miyo nodded. That was true. And even if Mr. Wickett couldn't understand Japanese, at least he could answer back, and maybe that was even better than having an intelligent rooster around.

Miyo was glad everything had turned out so well, and went to bed feeling good inside.

A Reader Says

I would've moved outside the city limits before I gave away my pet. Mr. Lincoln won't understand why he had to leave his home.

How did you feel about the story?

After You Read

Thinking About What You Read

1. Why do you think Mrs. K. finally decided to give Mr. Lincoln away?
2. Why do you think Miyo was surprised when Mr. Botts wanted the rooster?
3. Why do you think Mrs. K. invited Mr. Wickett to the party?
4. How do you know that Mr. Lincoln is going to a good home?

Thinking About How You Read

How did making a summary help you understand the main problem in the story and how it was solved?

Sharing and Listening

What would you do if a rooster woke a neighbor up at six o'clock each morning? How would you solve this problem? Discuss your ideas with your classmates. Listen carefully when others give their ideas.

Writing

Suppose a neighbor of yours had a pet that needed a home. Write an ad for your class newspaper describing the pet.

Understanding Social Studies Selections

Starting with What You Know

You know that made-up stories are called **fiction**. Information that is not made up is called **non-fiction**. Nonfiction contains **facts**. Facts are things that are true, such as how tall you are and in what country you live. What other facts do you know?

Thinking About Social Studies

Social studies is a kind of nonfiction. It gives facts about people in different parts of the world. It tells where they live and how they live together in groups. Social studies writing has the same parts as all nonfiction writing.

Topic: This is what the writing is about. Social studies is always about real people and real places.

Main Ideas: These are the important ideas you learn as you read. In social studies you learn important facts about people and places.

Features: These are things such as pictures and maps. In a social studies article, pictures show you what the people and the places look like. A map might show you the places in a town or city.

Before You Read

Look at the title and look at the pictures. Think of what you would like to learn about the people and the place.

As You Read

Read carefully. If some parts don't make sense to you, read them again. You may see words in dark print. Be sure you find out what these words mean. Ask yourself these questions as you read. The questions with blue diamonds are for any non-fiction. Those with red diamonds are for social studies.

Topic: ◆ What is the article about?
◆ What do I already know about the people and the place?

Main Ideas: ◆ What new facts am I learning?
◆ What are the important ideas about the people and the place?

Features: ◆ What do the pictures and the map show me about the people and the place?

Apply what you know about reading social studies selections as you read the two social studies selections that follow. Use the side notes to help you.

Over the past 2,000 years, Japan has changed in many ways. In other ways, however, Japan has stayed the same. In this article, you will read how traditions of the past are still part of a changing Japan.

Count Your Way
五 **Through** 六
Japan

by Jim Haskins

The title tells you the topic. Think of what you already know about Japan.

You might know that Japan makes computers and cars, but did you know that Japanese people still do many things they did almost 2,000 years ago? Even though Japan has changed so much, tradition is still very important. They elect officials just like we do, but they also have an emperor whose family ruled more than 1,000 years ago. The Japanese are good at mixing the old with the new.

This tells you what you will learn as you read.

The Japanese are also able to take things from other cultures and make them their own. Some of the customs you will read about, like using chopsticks and writing with a brush, came from China. Now they are a part of Japanese culture.

You can see that the Japanese are very good at changing with the world while still remaining Japanese. This article counts through the numbers one to ten as a way to show you the Japan of today.

1 ― ee-chee

There is only **one** Fujiyama, a mountain better known to Americans as Mount Fuji. It is the highest mountain in Japan. It is also the most often painted and photographed landmark in that country. Mount Fuji is a dormant volcano, which means that it has not erupted in a long time. In fact, the last time it erupted was in 1707. Mount Fuji is surrounded by five small lakes, one of which is noted for its reflection of the snowcapped mountain on its still waters. Thousands of people climb to the top of Mt. Fuji every summer.

This is the most important fact about Mount Fuji.

2 ニ nee

Two chopsticks are the traditional Japanese eating utensils. They are usually made from bamboo or wood. Each chopstick is about as thick as a pencil where it is held and thinner where the stick touches the food. Chopsticks are held in one hand and are used by moving the top stick up and down while the bottom stick remains still. Japanese children are taught how to use chopsticks when they are quite young.

3 三 sahn

Notice that each part of the story tells about a certain number of things — one, two, and so on.

Many Japanese people learn early in life that there are **three** things to fear in nature—earthquakes, fire, and typhoons.

The Japanese islands were formed when forces of the earth pushed them up from the ocean floor. These same forces continue to affect the islands by causing as many as 1,500 earthquakes each year.

Fires may burn out of control after a bad earthquake. Flames used for everyday cooking and heating can come in contact with falling timber, spreading fire quickly throughout a town.

A typhoon is a western Pacific storm. These storms' heavy rains and strong winds cause much damage across the Japanese islands, mostly during the months from July to October.

4 四 shee

The people make changes when the weather changes.

There are **four** seasons in a year. The seasons and other cycles of nature have a great influence on Japanese culture. When the season changes, *kimonos* (kih-MO-nuhz) often reflect this change. Kimonos are traditional, robelike pieces of clothing that originated with the Japanese. In the summer, a person might wear a *kimono* showing a pattern of morning glories. In the fall, the robe could display maple leaves. A winter *kimono* is sometimes made of material with a snowflake pattern, and early flowers might decorate a *kimono* in the spring. In this way, Japanese people can wear on their clothing the same patterns that decorate nature.

5 五 go

The *Noh* play is the oldest form of traditional Japanese theater. Japanese *Noh* theater combines words, music, and dance to tell stories about Japanese history and legend. *Noh* theater uses very few characters, and traditionally all the actors are men. There are **five** main categories of Japanese *Noh* plays:

(1) god plays (*Kami-mono*)

(2) battle plays (*Shura-mono*)

(3) stories of beautiful women (*Katsura-mono*. *Katsura* means wig; since all the actors in *Noh* plays are men, naturally whoever plays a woman has to wear a wig!)

(4) present-day plays (*Genzai-mono*)

(5) stories of evil forces (*Oni-mono*)

Stop here and think about what you have read so far. Predict what you will learn next.

6 六 ro-koo

There are **six** major *sumo* tournaments in Japan each year. *Sumo*, a Japanese form of wrestling, is a very popular spectator sport in Japan. The wrestlers are large men who weigh hundreds of pounds. In a *sumo* match, the wrestlers try to throw each other down to the ground. The average *sumo* match lasts only ten seconds, so there are many matches in each tournament.

7 七 shee-chee

Calligraphy, writing with a brush and ink, is a fine art in Japan. There are about 1,850 written characters in common use. These characters are combined to make up the Japanese language just as we use the letters of our alphabet to make up words. These characters are often divided up according to how many brush strokes it takes to make them.

The character for the words "how many" requires **seven** strokes.

How many　　何

This picture shows you more about the topic.

ノ
イ
イ
仁
行
何
何

122

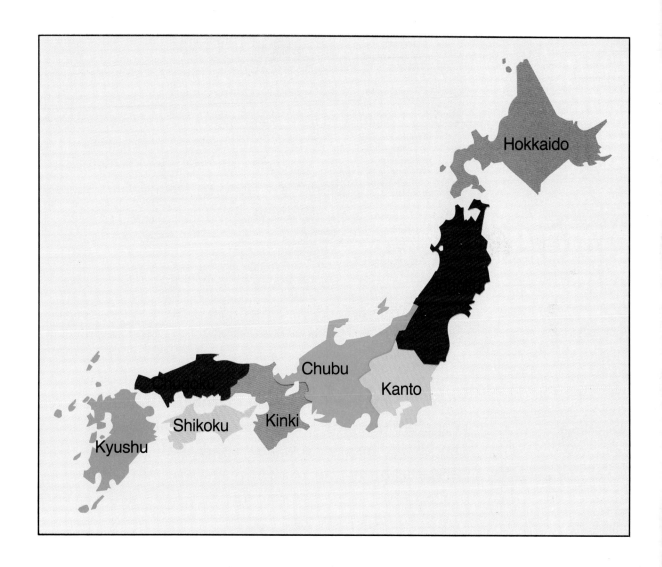

8 八 hah-chee

Japan is divided into **eight** major geographic regions. Three of them, Hokkaido, Shikoku, and Kyushu, are located on the islands of the same name and include the smaller offshore islands that surround them. The remaining five regions, Tohoku, Kanto, Chubu, Kinki, and Chugoku, are all on the island of Honshu. Honshu is the largest of the four main islands in the group of islands that makes up Japan.

Read slowly. The names are hard.

123

9 九 koo

In a traditional Japanese marriage ceremony, **nine** cups of rice wine are drunk, one right after another. The cups are very small and hold only about a thimbleful of wine. Japanese rice wine is called *sake*.

10 十 joo

Think about what you've learned. Read the hard parts again.

When they reach the age of **ten**, Japanese children must begin to take on new responsibilities. By that age, he or she is expected to start practicing to be an adult.

A Reader Says

I think ten is too young to start practicing to be an adult.

How did you feel about the article?

After You Read

Thinking About What You Read

1. Why do you think Mt. Fuji is so important in Japanese art?

2. Why do you think the weather and nature have great influence on Japanese culture?

3. Why do you think the Japanese enjoy the Noh plays?

4. How do you know the Japanese respect and honor tradition?

Thinking About How You Read

How did knowing this was a social studies article help you find the important facts and ideas about the people and culture of Japan?

Sharing and Listening

What old American traditions are still a part of American culture? Tell why you think some American traditions have remained even though our culture is changing. Listen to what your classmates think.

Writing

What is your favorite American tradition? Write a few sentences about the tradition. Tell why it is your favorite.

Writing
in a New Way

No one's handwriting is exactly the same. Perhaps you know someone whose writing you can hardly read, but you also might have a friend who writes very clearly and neatly. Some people write in a very fine way called calligraphy.

The word *calligraphy* comes from two Greek words: *kalos*, which means "beautiful" and *graphein*, which means "writing." Calligraphy is the art of beautiful handwriting, and a calligrapher is a person who practices this art.

Calligraphy is very old. It was developed into an art form by the Chinese more than 2,000 years ago. Later the Japanese learned calligraphy from their neighbors and became experts at it.

For the Japanese, calligraphy is like painting. In fact, they use the same kind of brush for both painting and calligraphy.

Japanese calligraphers often work on silk scrolls, but calligraphy is also used to decorate walls, books, newspapers, and buildings.

126

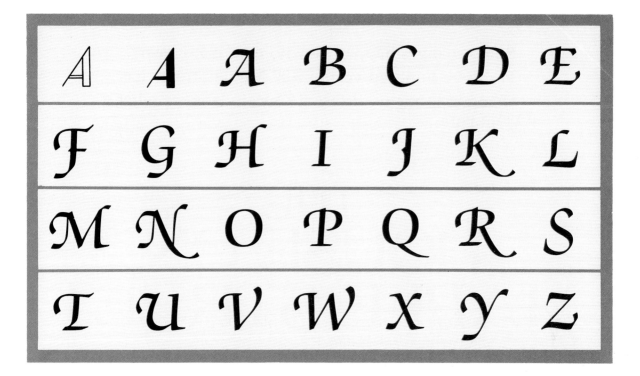

Would you like to be a calligrapher? You can do calligraphy in English. It just takes practice. Remember to work slowly and carefully.

1. First you'll need the paint, a brush, a piece of paper, and a pencil.

2. Think of a name or a short sentence you might like to write in calligraphy. Write each letter lightly in pencil. Make them all large.

3. Now add curls to the beginning of each letter. Try adding curls to the end of each letter too.

4. After you have finished decorating your name or sentence, you will be ready to paint. Choose a paint color you like.

5. Paint the outside of each letter thick and dark. You may need to use some pressure. Make the inside of each letter thin and light. Do not use a lot of pressure.

6. Now let the paint dry. Then roll the paper up so that it will look like a scroll.

When you have finished, perhaps you'd like to try another sentence. Design and paint it in any way you want.

Some changes happen slowly, over many years.
For three hundred years, "107 Maple Street" has
changed in many different ways to become what it
is today.

THE
HOUSE ON
MAPLE STREET

by Bonnie Pryor

This is 107 Maple Street. Chrissy and Jenny live here with their mother and father, a dog named Maggie, and a fat cat named Sally.

Three hundred years ago there was no house here or even a street. There was only a forest and a babbling spring where the animals came to drink.

One day a fierce storm roared across the forest. The sky rolled with thunder, and lightning crashed into a tree. A deer sniffed the air in alarm. Soon the woods were ablaze.

The next spring a few sturdy flowers poked through the ashes, and by the year after that the land was covered with grass. Some wildflowers grew at the edge of the stream where the deer had returned to drink.

One day the earth trembled, and a cloud of dust rose to the sky. A mighty herd of buffalo had come to eat the sweet grass and drink from the stream.

People came, following the buffalo herd. They set up their tepees near the stream. They liked it so much that they stayed for the whole summer.

One boy longed to be a great hunter like his father, but for now he could only pretend with his friends. In their games, one boy was chosen to be the buffalo.

His father taught him how to make an arrowhead and smooth it just so, the way his father had taught him. But the boy was young, and the day was hot.

He ran off to play with his friends and left the arrowhead on a rock. When he came back later to get it, he could not find it.

The buffalo moved on, searching for new grass, and the people packed up their tepees and followed.

For a long time the land was quiet. Some rabbits made their home in the stump of a burned tree, and a fox made a den in some rocks.

One day there was a new sound. The fox looked up. A wagon train passed by, heading for California. The settlers stopped beside the stream for a night. But they dreamed of gold and places far away and were gone the next morning.

Other wagons came, following the tracks of the first. The fox family moved into the woods.

Soon after, a man and a woman camped along the stream. They were heading west, but the woman would soon have a child. They looked around them and knew it was a good place to stay. The man cut down trees and made a house.

He pulled up tree stumps left from the fire and planted his crops. The child was a girl, and they named her Ruby and called her their little jewel.

Ruby had a set of china dishes that she played with every day. One day when she was making a mudpie near a stream, she found an arrowhead buried deep in the ground. She put it in a cup to show her father when he came in from the fields.

Ruby's mother called her to watch the new baby. While she was gone, a rabbit sniffed at the cup and knocked it off the rock. It fell into the tunnel to his burrow, and the rabbit moved away to a new home under the roots of a tree.

Ruby grew up and moved away, but her brother stayed on the farm. By now there were other people nearby, and he married a girl from another farm. They had six children, and he built a larger house so they would all fit.

Now the old wagon trail was used as a road, and the dust got into the house. When his wife complained, Ruby's brother planted a row of maple trees along the road to keep out the dust and shade the house. After the children were grown, he and his wife moved away, but one of their daughters stayed on the farm with her husband and children.

One day the children's great-aunt Ruby came for
a visit. She was an old lady with snow-white hair.
The children loved to hear her stories of long ago.
She told them about the cup and arrowhead she
had lost when she was a girl.

After she left, the children looked and looked.
They searched for days, but they never found them.

The town had grown nearly to the edge of the
farm, and another man up the road filled in the
stream and changed its course. For a while there
was a trickle of water in the spring when the snow
melted, but dirt filled in the bed, until hardly
anyone remembered a stream had ever been there.

New people lived on the farm. It was the schoolteacher and his family, and they sold much of the land to others. The road was paved with bricks, so there was no longer any dust, but the maple trees remained. The branches hung down over the road, making it shady and cool. People called it Maple Street. Automobiles drove on the road, along with carts and wagons, and there were many new houses.

The house was crumbling and old, and one day some men tore it down. For a while again, the land was bare. The rabbits lived comfortably, with only an occasional owl or fox to chase them. But one day a young couple came walking along and stopped to admire the trees.

"What a wonderful place for a home," said the young woman. So they hired carpenters and masons to build a cozy house of red bricks with white trim.

The young couple lived happily in the house for several years. The young man got a job in another town, and they had to move.

The house was sold to a man and a woman who had two girls named Chrissy and Jenny and a dog named Maggie, and a fat cat named Sally.

The girls helped their father dig up a spot of ground for a garden, but it was Maggie the dog who dug up something white in the soft spring earth.

"Stop," cried Chrissy, and she picked up the tiny cup made of china. Inside was the arrowhead found and lost so long ago.

"Who lost these?" the girls wondered. Chrissy and Jenny put the cup and arrowhead on a shelf for others to see. Someday perhaps their children will play with the tiny treasures and wonder about them, too. But the cup and the arrowhead will forever keep their secrets, and the children can only dream.

A Reader Says

Chrissy and Jenny should leave something of theirs behind for someone else to find.

How did you feel about the story?

After You Read

Thinking About What You Read

1. Why do you think people decide to settle in a place?
2. Why do you think people finally decide to move on to a new place?
3. How do you know that everyday happenings help to make up the history of a place?
4. Why do you think that Chrissy and Jenny were curious about the arrowhead and china cup?

Thinking About How You Read

How did asking yourself questions help you understand how 107 Maple Street changed?

Sharing and Listening

How do you think the area where you live has changed over time? Think about what the land your school is on looked like one hundred years ago. Who lived there? What sort of things might they have left behind? Share your ideas with your classmates.

Writing

What would you like people of the future to know about you? Write a short letter telling about yourself and your life. Tell about the things *you* would leave for others to find.

Ramona has always been the baby of the family.
Now that's about to change forever.

RAMONA and the BIG EVENT

◆

by Beverly Cleary

"Girls, please stop moping around," said Mrs.
Quimby.

"We can't find anything to do," said Beezus.

Ramona was silent. If she complained, her
mother would tell her to clean out her closet.

"Read a book," said Mrs. Quimby. "Both of you,
read a book."

136

"I've read all my books a million times," said Ramona, who usually enjoyed rereading her favorites.

"Then go to the library." Mrs. Quimby was beginning to sound irritable.

"It's too hot," complained Ramona.

Mrs. Quimby glanced at her watch.

"Mother, are you expecting someone?" asked Ramona. "You keep looking at your watch."

"I certainly am," said her mother. With a big sigh, Mrs. Quimby sank heavily to the couch, glanced at her watch again, and closed her eyes. The girls exchanged guilty looks. Their poor mother, worn out by the baby kicking her when there was so much of her to feel hot.

"Mother, are you all right?" Beezus sounded worried.

"I'm fine," snapped Mrs. Quimby, which surprised the girls into behaving.

That evening, the sisters helped their mother put together a cold supper of tuna fish salad and tomatoes. While the family was eating, Mr. Quimby told them that now that the "Hawaiian Holidays" sale with bargains in fresh pineapple and papaya had come to an end, his market was preparing for "Western Bar-b-q Week" with specials on steak, baked beans, tomato sauce, and chili. He planned to paint bucking broncos on the front window.

Mrs. Quimby nibbled at her salad and glanced at her watch.

"And everybody will see your paintings," said Ramona, happy that her father was now an artist as well as a market manager.

"Not quite the same as an exhibit in a museum," said Mr. Quimby, who did not sound as happy as Ramona expected.

Mrs. Quimby pushed her chair farther from the table and glanced at her watch. All eyes were on her.

"Shall I call the doctor?" asked Mr. Quimby.

"Please," said Mrs. Quimby as she rose from the table, and breathed, "Oo-oo."

Ramona and Beezus, excited and frightened, looked at one another. At last! The fifth Quimby would soon be here. Nothing would be the same again, ever. Mr. Quimby reported that the doctor would meet them at the hospital. Without being asked, Beezus ran for the bag her mother had packed several weeks ago.

Mrs. Quimby kissed her daughters. "Don't look so frightened," she said. "Everything is going to be all right. Be good girls, and Daddy will be home as soon as he can."

The house suddenly seemed empty. The girls
listened to the car back out of the driveway. The
sound of the motor became lost in traffic.

"Well," said Beezus, "I suppose we might as well
do the dishes."

"I suppose so." Ramona tested all the doors,
including the door to the basement, to make sure
they were locked.

To her own surprise, Ramona burst into tears
and buried her face in a dish towel. "I just want
Mother to come home," she wept.

Beezus wiped her soapy hands on the seat of her
cutoff jeans. Then she put her arms around
Ramona, something she had never done before.
"Don't worry, Ramona. Everything will be all right,
Mother said so, and I remember when you came."

Ramona felt better. A big sister could be a comfort if she wanted to.

"You were born and Mother was fine." Beezus handed Ramona a clean dish towel.

Minutes crawled by. The long Oregon dusk turned into night. The girls turned on the television set to a program about people in a hospital, running, shouting, giving orders. Quickly they turned it off.

The ring of the telephone made Ramona feel as if arrows of electricity had shot through her stomach as Beezus ran to answer.

"Oh." There was disappointment in Beezus's voice. "All right, Daddy. No. No, we don't mind." When the conversation ended, she turned to Ramona, who was wild for news, and said, "The baby is taking his time. Daddy wants to stay with Mom and wanted to be sure we didn't mind staying alone. I said we didn't, and he said we were brave girls."

"Oh," said Ramona, who longed for her father's return. "Well, I'm brave, I guess." Even though it was unusually warm, she closed all the windows.

"I suppose we should go to bed," said Beezus. "If you want, you can get in bed with me."

"We better leave lights on for Daddy." Ramona turned on the porch light, as well as all the lights in the living room and hall, before she climbed into her sister's bed. "So Daddy won't fall over anything," she explained.

"Good idea," agreed Beezus. Each sister knew the other felt safer with the lights on.

"I hope the baby will hurry," said Ramona.

"So do I," agreed Beezus.

The girls slept lightly until the sound of a key in the door awoke them. "Daddy?" Beezus called out.

"Yes." Mr. Quimby came to the door of Beezus's room. "Great news. Roberta Day Quimby, six pounds, four ounces, arrived safe and sound. Your mother is fine."

Barely awake, Ramona asked, "Who's Roberta?"

"Your new sister," answered her father, "and my namesake."

"*Sister*." Now Ramona was wide-awake. The family had referred to the baby as *he* so long she had assumed that of course she would have a brother.

"Yes, a beautiful little sister," said her father. "Now, go back to sleep. It's four o'clock in the morning, and I've got to get up at seven."

The next morning, Mr. Quimby overslept and ate his breakfast standing up. He was halfway out the

142

door when he called back, "When I get off work,
we'll have dinner, and then we'll all go see Roberta
and your mother."

The day was long and lonely. Even a swimming
lesson at the park and a trip to the library did little
to make time pass. "I wonder what Roberta looks
like?" said Beezus.

"And whose room she will share when she
outgrows the bassinette?" worried Ramona.

The one happy moment in the day for the girls
was a telephone call from their mother, who
reported that Roberta was a beautiful, healthy little
sister. She couldn't wait to bring her home, and
she was proud of her daughters for being so good
about staying alone. This pleased Beezus and
Ramona so much they ran the vacuum cleaner and
dusted, which made time pass faster until their
father, looking exhausted, came home to take them
out for hamburgers and a visit to the fifth Quimby.

Ramona could feel her heart pounding as she climbed the steps to the hospital. Visitors, some carrying flowers and others looking careworn, walked toward the elevators. Nurses hurried, a doctor was paged over the loudspeaker. Ramona could scarcely bear her own excitement. The rising of the elevator made her stomach feel as if it had stayed behind on the first floor. When the elevator stopped, Mr. Quimby led the way down the hall.

"Excuse me," called a nurse.

Surprised, the family stopped and turned.

"Children under twelve are not allowed to visit the maternity ward," said the nurse. "Little girl, you will have to go down and wait in the lobby."

"Why is that?" asked Mr. Quimby.

"Children under twelve might have contagious diseases," explained the nurse. "We have to protect the babies."

"I'm sorry, Ramona," said Mr. Quimby. "I didn't know. I am afraid you will have to do as the nurse says."

"Does she mean I'm *germy*?" Ramona was humiliated. "I took a shower this morning and washed my hands after dinner so I would be extra clean."

"Sometimes children are coming down with something and don't know it," explained Mr. Quimby. "Now, be a big girl and go downstairs and wait for us."

Ramona's eyes filled with tears of disappointment, but she found some pleasure in riding in the elevator alone. By the time she reached the lobby, she felt worse. The nurse called her a little girl. Her father called her a big girl. What was she? A germy girl.

Ramona sat gingerly on the edge of a couch. If she leaned back, she might get germs on her. She swallowed hard. Was her throat a little bit sore? She thought maybe it was, way down in back. She put her hand to her forehead the way her mother did when she thought Ramona might have a fever. Her forehead was warm, maybe too warm.

As Ramona waited, she began to itch the way she itched when she had chickenpox. Her head itched, her back itched, her legs itched. Ramona scratched. A woman sat down on the couch, looked at Ramona, got up, and moved to another couch.

Ramona felt worse. She itched more and scratched harder. She swallowed often to see how her sore throat was coming along. She peeked down the neck of her blouse to see if she might have a rash and was surprised that she did not. She sniffed from time to time to see if she had a runny nose.

Now Ramona was angry. It would serve everybody right if she came down with some horrible disease, right there in their old hospital. That would show everybody how germfree the place was. Ramona squirmed and gave that hard-to-reach place between her shoulder blades a good hard scratch. Then she scratched her head with both hands. People stopped to stare.

A man in a white coat, with a stethoscope hanging out of his pocket, came hurrying through the lobby, glanced at Ramona, stopped, and took a good look at her. "How do you feel?" he asked.

"Awful," she admitted. "A nurse said I was too germy to go see my mother and new sister, but I think I caught some disease right here."

"I see," said the doctor. "Open your mouth and say 'ah.'"

Ramona *ahhed* until she gagged.

"Mh-hm," murmured the doctor. He looked so serious Ramona was alarmed. Then he pulled out his stethoscope and listened to her front and back, thumping as he did so. What was he hearing? Was there something wrong with her insides? Why didn't her father come?

The doctor nodded as if his worst suspicions had been confirmed. "Just as I thought," he said, pulling out his prescription pad.

Medicine, ugh. Ramona's twitching stopped. Her nose and throat felt fine. "I feel much better," she assured the doctor as she eyed that prescription pad with distrust.

"An acute case of siblingitis. Not at all unusual around here, but it shouldn't last long." He tore off the prescription he had written, instructed Ramona to give it to her father, and hurried on down the hall.

Ramona could not remember the name of her illness. She tried to read the doctor's scribbly cursive writing, but she could not. She could only read neat cursive, the sort her teacher wrote on the blackboard.

Itching again, she was still staring at the slip of paper when Mr. Quimby and Beezus stepped out of the elevator. "Roberta is so tiny." Beezus was radiant with joy. "And she is perfectly darling. She has a little round nose and—oh, when you see her, you'll love her."

"I'm sick." Ramona tried to sound pitiful. "I've got something awful. A doctor said so."

Beezus paid no attention. "And Roberta has brown hair—"

Mr. Quimby interrupted. "What's this all about, Ramona?"

"A doctor said I had something, some kind of *itis*, and I have to have this right away." She handed her father her prescription and scratched one shoulder. "If I don't, I might get sicker."

Mr. Quimby read the scribbly cursive, and then
he did a strange thing. He lifted Ramona and gave
her a big hug and a kiss, right there in the lobby.
The itching stopped. Ramona felt much better.
"You have acute siblingitis," explained her father.
"*Itis* means inflammation."

Ramona already knew the meaning of sibling.
Since her father had studied to be a teacher,
brothers and sisters had become siblings to him.

"He understood you were worried and angry because you weren't allowed to see your new sibling, and prescribed attention," explained Mr. Quimby. "Now let's go home before I fall asleep standing up."

Beezus said Roberta was too darling to be called a dumb word like sibling. Ramona felt silly, but she also felt better.

For the next three nights, Ramona took a book to the hospital and sat in the lobby, not reading, but sulking about the injustice of having to wait to see the strange new Roberta.

On the fourth day, Mr. Quimby took an hour off from the market, picked up Beezus and Ramona, who were waiting in clean clothes, and drove to the hospital to bring home his wife and new daughter.

Ramona moved closer to Beezus when she saw her mother, holding a pink bundle, emerge from the elevator in a wheelchair pushed by a nurse and followed by Mr. Quimby carrying her bag. "Can't Mother walk?" she whispered.

"Of course she can walk," answered Beezus. "The hospital wants to make sure people get out without falling down and suing for a million dollars."

Mrs. Quimby waved to the girls. Roberta's face was hidden by a corner of a pink blanket, but the nurse had no time for a little girl eager to see a new baby. She pushed the wheelchair through the automatic door to the waiting car.

"*Now* can I see her?" begged Ramona when her mother and Roberta were settled in the front, and the girls had climbed into the backseat.

"Dear Heart, of course you may." Mrs. Quimby then spoke the most beautiful words Ramona had ever heard, "Oh, Ramona, how I've missed you." Ramona, leaning over the front seat for her first glimpse of the new baby sister, tried to hold her breath so she wouldn't breathe germs on Roberta, who did not look at all like the picture on the cover of *A Name for Your Baby*. Her face was bright pink, almost red, and her hair, unlike the smooth pale hair of the baby on the cover of the pamphlet, was dark and wild. Ramona did not know what to say. She did not feel that words like darling or adorable fitted this baby.

"She looks exactly like you looked when you were born," Mrs. Quimby told Ramona.

"She does?" Ramona found this hard to believe. She could not imagine that she had once looked like this red, frowning little creature.

"Well, what do you think of your new sister?" asked Mr. Quimby.

"She's so—so *little*," Ramona answered truthfully.

Roberta opened her blue gray eyes.

"Mother!" cried Ramona. "She's cross-eyed."

Mrs. Quimby laughed. "All babies look cross-eyed sometimes. They outgrow it when they learn to focus." Sure enough, Roberta's eyes straightened out for a moment and then crossed again. She worked her mouth as if she didn't know what to do with it. She made little snuffling noises and lifted one arm as if she didn't know what it was for.

"Why does her nightie have those little pockets at the end of the sleeves?" asked Ramona. "They cover up her hands."

"They keep her from scratching herself," explained Mrs. Quimby. "She's too little to understand that fingernails scratch."

Ramona sat back and buckled her seat belt. She had once looked like Roberta. Amazing! She had once been that tiny, but she had grown, her hair had calmed down when she remembered to comb it, and she had learned to use her eyes and hands. "You know what I think?" she asked and did not wait for an answer. "I think it is hard work to be a baby." Ramona spoke as if she had discovered something unknown to the rest of the world. With her words came unexpected love and sympathy for the tiny person in her mother's arms.

"I hadn't thought of it that way," said Mrs. Quimby, "but I think you're right."

"Growing up is hard work," said Mr. Quimby as he drove away from the hospital. "Sometimes being grown-up is hard work."

"I know," said Ramona and thought some more. She thought about loose teeth, real sore throats, quarrels, misunderstandings with her teachers, longing for a bicycle her family could not afford, worrying when her parents bickered, how terrible she felt when she hurt Beezus's feelings without meaning to, and all the long afternoons when Mrs. Kemp looked after her until her mother came from work. She had survived it all. "Isn't it funny?" she remarked as her father steered the car into their driveway.

"Isn't what funny?" asked her mother.

"That I used to be little and funny-looking and cross-eyed like Roberta," said Ramona. "And now look at me. I'm wonderful me!"

"Except when you're blunderful you," said Beezus.

Ramona did not mind when her family, except Roberta, who was too little, laughed. "Yup, wonderful, blunderful me," she said and was happy. She was winning at growing up.

A Reader Says

I think Ramona will be a good big sister for Roberta. She remembers what it's like to be little and can help Roberta grow up.

How did you feel about the story?

About the Author

Beverly Cleary

Beverly Cleary was born in Oregon and lived for awhile on a farm. When she was young, her mother used to read stories and poems aloud to her. Soon she began to love books.

At first she did not like learning to read in school. But in the third grade, she suddenly found out that reading was fun. She wanted to write books like those she enjoyed.

When she grew up, she worked in a library. Then, after she married, she wrote her first book, *Henry Huggins*. Since then she has written dozens of books. Some of them are *Henry and Beezus* and *Ramona Forever*. Mrs. Cleary has won many awards for her books about ordinary boys and girls.

When she writes, Mrs. Cleary thinks about the little girl inside herself. Mrs. Cleary, who now lives in California, believes that writing has to be fun. Then the reader will have fun, too. She wants children to enjoy her books. She is happiest when people tell her that her stories have helped children to enjoy reading. She uses humor and characters like Ramona to tell about the growing pains everyone goes through, and the feelings and problems of real children.

More Books About Changes

Annie and the Old One
by Miska Miles
Annie is a little girl who has a grandmother she loves very much. They have lived together on the reservation since Annie was born. Now it's time for Annie to learn that things can't stay the same forever.

From Path to Highway: The Story of the Boston Post Road
by Gail Gibbons
Here's another book that tells you how one place has changed over the years. The Boston Post Road started out as a dirt trail. Can you imagine what it's like today?

The Magic Listening Cap
by Yoshiko Uchida
Many of these folktales from Japan tell about ordinary people. But when these people meet up with magic, gods, and unusual animals, their lives change in extraordinary ways.

The Nightingale
by Hans Christian Andersen, translated by Eva Le Gallienne, illustrated by Nancy Ekholm Burkert
An emperor seems like one of the most powerful men in the world. But in this fairy tale, a little bird changes the life of China's mightiest ruler.

MAKING ALL THE
CONNECTIONS

Speaking and Listening

In this part of the book, you read stories about change. You read about how a new baby changed Ramona. You read about how moving to a new town changed life for Michael and his family. You also read about how a forest where only animals lived changed into Maple Street, where many families live. Think about these different kinds of changes. You may want to look at your Reader's Log first. Discuss them with your classmates. Speak loudly and clearly when you present your ideas. Listen carefully to the ideas of others. Use these questions to help you.

1. How did the life of each character you read about change?

2. Think about changes that you have noticed since you started school. How are they like the changes you read about in this part of the book?

3. Do you think that all of the changes you read about were for the better? Why or why not? Discuss your ideas with your classmates.

Reading Something New in Social Studies

Franklin Delano Roosevelt was the 32nd President of the United States. He was our President for twelve years. Read this story to learn about a great change in his life.

Franklin Roosevelt was a lucky young boy. He had wealthy parents and grew up having everything. He was taught that wealthy people should help those who were not as lucky.

When Franklin was grown up, he decided to run for public office. He was elected to the New York State Senate. A few years later, President Wilson asked Franklin to come to Washington and help him. Franklin's life was very successful. Then, something happened that changed it all.

Franklin went on a vacation with his wife Eleanor. They went sailing and swimming. He caught a chill and felt sick. Franklin discovered he could not move his legs. He had polio and would never walk again. Everyone thought Franklin's career was over. They said he would never be able to stand up and make a speech again. They were wrong.

Franklin Roosevelt did stand. He worked hard to make his arms strong enough to support his whole body. He returned to work. Soon, he was elected Governor of New York. Then, only eleven years after he became ill, Roosevelt was elected President of the United States.

Thinking About Changes

The story you just read about President Franklin Roosevelt was like the stories you have read in this part of the book. It is a story about change. It tells about a change in the life of Franklin Roosevelt and how it affected him. Think about the stories you have read. What changes did you read about? How did they affect the people in the stories? Copy this chart and use what you have read to complete it.

Person	Change	Effect
Franklin Roosevelt		
Ramona		
Michael		
Mrs. Kitamura		
The boy in *Gila Monsters Meet You at the Airport*		

Look back at your chart. You can see that there are all kinds of changes. Some changes can even be fun. Think about a change that was fun for you. Maybe you would like to write about it. Add it to the chart. Write your name in the column marked *Person*. Then complete the rest of the chart. You can add more than one fun change to your chart and decide which you want to write about later. You probably have a lot of good ideas. Write them in the chart.

Writing a Friendly Letter

In this part of the book, you have read about many different kinds of changes. Now it is your turn to write a friendly letter about a change and how its effect was fun for you. You can use the letter in *Where the Bear Went over the Mountain* on page 49 of this book as an example. Your Handbook also tells more about a friendly letter.

Planning

Begin by studying the features of a friendly letter.

- A friendly letter shares news with a friend or family member.
- It is written in a friendly way.
- It has a **heading**, a **greeting**, a **body**, a **closing**, and a **signature**.

Decide what you are going to write about. Use the chart you filled out to help you. Then decide who you are going to write to.

Composing

Now it is time to write your first draft.

- Brainstorm your ideas with a classmate.
- Think about what you will write about in your letter, and how you will present the information.
- Think of details that you think will be interesting to read.

Proofreading Marks

∧ add

✗ take out

≡ capitalize

₣ indent

Tim puts two sentences with the same subject together.

Tim adds the words *at first* to make the information more exact.

Too many sentences begin with *I*. Tim changes the way one sentence begins.

Revising

Now that you have written your first draft, your next step is to revise what you have written. Use the following checklist to help you.

Revising Checklist
- ✔ Have I included all the features of a friendly letter?
- ✔ Can I combine subjects and predicates to make new sentences?
- ✔ Have I included exact information?
- ✔ Can I add information to make my work complete?
- ✔ Where can I vary the beginnings of sentences?

Tim has written a first draft of a friendly letter. He is going to revise it. Tim uses the Revising Checklist, and uses proofreading marks to show his corrections.

Sleepaway camp is over. I had to clean my trunk, and I had to make my bed. At first I hated that, but my bunkmates made it fun. The prize was the best cleaner got a prize. I won! I got a broom-shaped medal. I gess you could say I went to sweepaway camp.

Proofreading

Now that you have revised your friendly letter, your next step is to revise punctuation and spelling. The following checklist will help you.

♦──♦

Proofreading Checklist
✔ Did my sentences begin with capital letters?
✔ Did I use correct end marks for my sentences?
✔ Did I use commas correctly?
✔ Is my capitalization and punctuation correct for all my
  abbreviations?

♦──♦

Tim looks at his friendly letter again. He checks
mistakes in spelling, punctuation, and capitalization.
He uses the Proofreading Checklist to help him.

> 12 Grove St.
> Provo, Utah
> September 4, 19—
>
> Dear Billy,
>   Sleepaway camp is over. I had to
> clean my bunk, and I had to make my bed. At first I
> hated that, but my bunkmates made it fun.
> The prize was the best cleaner got a prize. I won!
> I got a broom-shaped medal. I guess you
> could say I went to sweepaway camp.
>   Your cousin,
>   Tim

Tim places commas
in the heading and
the greeting.

Tim fixes mistakes
in capitalization and
spelling.

Tim places a
comma after the
closing.

Presenting

First, make a neat copy of your revised friendly
letter. Then share your friendly letter in these ways.
Reading aloud: Read your letter to the class.
Vote for the letters you like best.
Illustrate your letter: Draw a picture to show
something that you have written about. Display
your illustrated letters on the bulletin board.

163

PART THREE

Other Times

Our history sings of centuries
Such varying songs it sings!
It starts with winds, slow moving sails,
It ends with skies and wings.

Our History Sings
by Catherine Cate Coblentz

◆

Some of the people in this section are looking back
and learning about how it was in other times.
You'll also read about people and animals who
really lived long ago. As you read, think: How are
their lives different from yours today?

Exploring Words About Other Times

Starting with What You Know

When you think of other times, what ideas come to mind? Do you think of when you were a baby, or do you think of dinosaurs? The words in the box below tell about other times. Use these words and words of your own to answer the questions after the box.

old days	history	long ago
old	surprising	old fashioned
the past	different	prehistoric

When people talk about other times they are talking about history. How would you describe other times? Many things from the past are interesting or unusual. How would you describe some things from the past?

Building a Word Map

The word map shows how some of the words in the box above go together. Think about words you can add to the map. Use words from the box and other words of your own.

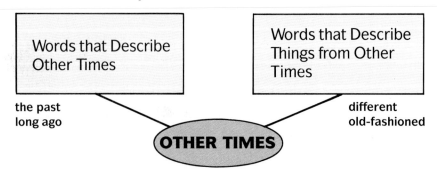

Words that Describe Other Times

Words that Describe Things from Other Times

the past
long ago

different
old-fashioned

OTHER TIMES

Finishing a Story

Look at the story below. The story tells about a boy who likes to learn about other times. Some words are missing. Think of the words you would use to finish the story.

Use the words from the box and word map in this lesson for ideas. Complete the story.

My grandfather lives in a(n) _____ house in the country. I like to look through my grandfather's _____ things. They tell me a lot about _____.

I found a photo album. The pictures in it were _____. There was a photo of grandfather when he was young. His clothes seemed _____. In one photo grandfather was driving a(n) _____ _____. Grandfather often tells me stories of his past. One day, I will tell these stories to my _____.

Share your story with your classmates. What words did you use? How did the stories differ?

As You Read

In this part of the book, you will read about animals and people who lived long ago. Keeping a Reader's Log will help you remember important thoughts, ideas, and words. As you read, make notes in your log. You could begin your Reader's Log with the chart. Add new words to the chart as you find them.

167

Old things can make us curious about the people who used them long ago. A trip to an auction makes Dudley wonder about other times.

DUDLEY
and the Auction

◆

by Philip Ressner

One windy, starlit night that made you want to run down the dark road and jump at the sky, Dudley went with his parents to an auction. It was in a hot, crowded barn full of old furniture, books, junk, and people.

The auctioneer, who was selling the things, stood on a box at one end of the barn. In no time he had talked people into buying an old chest of drawers with no drawers, an old two-handled saw, and a box of old yellowed dishes with little blue flowers around their edges that some people had probably eaten out of fifty times a thousand times.

"Why do people want all those old, used things?" Dudley asked.

"Well, some of them are beautiful," his father said.

"And some of them are useful," his mother said.

"What about the rest of them?" Dudley asked.

His father said, "*All* those things remind us of all the people who lived in the world before us."

"Then someday," Dudley said, "maybe a hundred years from now, somebody might buy the baby's cradle or my yellow cocoa mug and keep it on a shelf and look at it and wonder who *we* were?"

"Or even *my* old cocoa mug, that I still have and that has a picture of Orphan Annie on it," Dudley's father said.

"Or my yellow bicycle," Dudley's mother said. "Or the green porcelain flowerpot with the handles."

"And they'll think about us," Dudley said, "and how we must have once used all those things."

"Yes," Dudley's mother said, "even though they never knew us or even our names."

"Who'll give me ten dollars for this beautiful old mirror?" said the auctioneer, holding up a beautiful old mirror.

"Bet that old mirror has reflected a million things," Dudley's father said, and held up his hand. "Five dollars," he called to the auctioneer.

"First thing when I get home," Dudley said, "I'm going to put my name on the bottom of my yellow mug."

Thinking About the Theme

1. Dudley hopes that someday someone will buy his mug and know that, long ago, it belonged to him. What do you have that you'd like someone to have a hundred years from now?

2. Some things from other times aren't made anymore. Can you think of something you might find at an auction that you couldn't buy in a store that sold new things?

Making Comparisons

Starting with What You Know

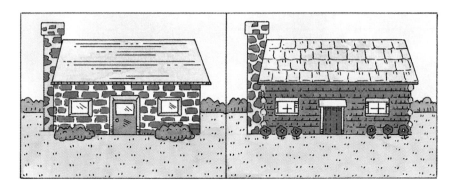

How are the two houses above alike? How are they different?

Thinking About Comparisons

A **comparison** shows how two things are alike or different. Writers often make comparisons to help you see what they are describing. They may use clue words such as *like*, *as*, *but*, *however*, or *different* to compare things.

Read the paragraph below. What two things are being compared? What are the clue words?

> The inside of Mr. Wilson's house was like the inside of Mrs. Carter's house. Mr. Wilson's house, however, was made of logs, and Mrs. Carter's house was made of bricks. Mr. Wilson planted flowers in front of his cabin, but Mrs. Carter planted small bushes.

The writer compares Mr. Wilson's house and Mrs. Carter's house. The clue words are *like*, *however*, and *but*.

Practice

Read each paragraph. Find the words that are clues to comparisons. Tell what two things are being compared and how they are alike or different.

1. For a moment, the two kites flew side by side. Kim's kite was green and shaped like a box. Dudley's kite was green, too, but it had a different shape. It was shaped like a diamond. The tail on Kim's kite was made of yellow ribbon. The tail on Dudley's kite, however, was made from two of his father's old blue ties.

2. Angela pulled two marbles from the small bag. One was white with blue swirls, but the other was clear with a thin band of green through it. The clear one was like one of Henry's marbles. It was called a "cat's eye." However, Angela thought the white one was prettier.

As You Read

Noticing comparisons will help you see what the writer is describing. You can also make your own comparisons while you read and after you read. Ask yourself these questions:

- What clue words are there?
- What two things are being compared?
- How are they alike or different?
- Are there other things in the story I can compare?

Apply what you know about making comparisons as you read the two selections that follow. Use the side notes to help you.

Long ago, many people left their homelands to come to the new world of America. When Pettranella sets out with her parents for her new country, she makes a promise to the grandmother who stays behind.

Pettranella

by Betty Waterton

Long ago in a country far away lived a little girl named Pettranella. She lived with her father and mother in the upstairs of her grandmother's tall, narrow house.

One dark winter night, Pettranella's father came home with a letter. The family gathered around the table in the warm yellow circle of the lamp to read it. Even her grandmother came up to listen.

"It's from Uncle Gus in America," began her father. "He has his homestead there now, and is already clearing his land. Someday it will be a large farm growing many crops of grain."

Think about how Uncle Gus's home is different from Pettranella's.

174

When he had finished reading the letter aloud,
Pettranella said, "I wish we could go there, too,
and live on a homestead."

Her parents looked at each other, their eyes
twinkling with a secret. "We *are* going," said her
mother. "We are sailing on the very next ship."

Pettranella could hardly believe her ears.
Suddenly she thought of some things she had
always wanted. "Can we have some chickens?" she
asked. "And a swing?"

"You will be in charge of the chickens," laughed
her father, "and I will put up a swing for you in
our biggest tree."

"And Grandmother," cried Pettranella, "now you
will have a real flower garden, not just a window
box."

Pulling her close, her grandmother said gently, "But I cannot go to the new land with you, little one. I am too old to make such a long journey."

Pettranella's eyes filled with tears. "Then I won't go either," she said.

But in the end, of course she did.

When they were ready to leave, her grandmother gave her a small muslin bag. Pettranella opened it and peered inside. "There are seeds in here!" she exclaimed.

"There's a garden in there," said her grandmother. "Those are flower seeds to plant when you arrive at your new home."

"Oh, I will take such good care of them," promised Pettranella, "and plant them in a beautiful garden for you."

So they left their homeland. It was sad, thought Pettranella, but it was exciting, too. Sad to say good-bye to everyone they knew, and exciting to be going across the ocean in a big ship.

At last they reached the shores of Canada. Then they traveled up a wide river and across the lonely land.

After many days they came to a settlement, where two rivers met. There they camped while her father got his homestead papers. Then they bought some things they would need: an axe and a saw, a hammer and nails, sacks of food and seed, a plow and a cow and a strong brown ox, and a cart with two large wooden wheels. And some chickens.

The ox was hitched to the cart, which was full of all their belongings.

Predict what the family will do when they reach their land.

176

One day as they followed the narrow winding trail through groves of spruce and poplar, there was a sudden THUMP, CRACK, CRASH!

"What happened?" cried Pettranella.

"We have broken a shaft," said her father, "because one of the wheels went over a big rock."

They began to unload the cart. "We'll make a new shaft," said her father; and, taking his axe, he went into the woods to cut a pole that would fit.

Pettranella helped her mother fix lunch, then sat down on a log to wait. Taking the bag of seeds from her pocket, she poured them out into a little pile on her lap, thinking all the while of the garden she would soon be making.

Just then she heard a familiar creaking and squeaking, and it was getting closer. It had to be another ox cart!

"Somebody's coming!" she shouted, jumping up.

Her father came running out of the woods as the cart drew near. It was just like theirs, but the ox was black. The driver had a tanned, friendly face. When he saw their trouble, he swung down from his cart to help.

He helped her father make a new shaft, then they fastened it in place and loaded the cart again.

Afterwards they all had lunch and talked together. Their new friend said that he had a homestead nearby and he invited them to visit one day.

"Do you have any children?" asked Pettranella.

"A little girl just like you," he laughed, as he climbed into his cart. Pettranella waved good-bye as he drove off, and they set forth once again to find their homestead. "Our neighbor says it isn't far now," said her father.

As they bumped along the trail, suddenly Pettranella thought about the flower seeds. She felt in her pocket, but there was nothing there. The muslin bag was gone!

"Oh, oh! Stop!" she cried. "The seeds are gone!"

Her father halted the ox. "I saw you looking at them before lunch," said her mother. "You must have spilled them there."

"I'm going back to look," said Pettranella, and before they could stop her, she was running back down the trail.

She found the log, but she didn't find any seeds. Just the empty muslin bag.

As she trudged back to the cart, her tears began to fall. "I was going to make such a lovely garden, and now I broke my promise to Grandmother!"

"Maybe you can make a vegetable garden instead," suggested her mother, but Pettranella knew it wouldn't be the same. "I don't think turnips and cabbages are very pretty," she sighed.

Instead is a clue word. Mother compares a vegetable garden with the one Pettranella would have planted.

It was later that afternoon when they found their homestead.

Their own land, as far as they could see! Pettranella was so excited that for a while she forgot all about her lost seeds.

The next morning her father began to put up a small cabin. Then he started to break the land. A small piece of ground was set aside for vegetables, and after it was dug, it was Pettranella's job to rake the soil and gather the stones into a pile.

"Now we can plant the garden," said her mother, and they did.

A few days later when Pettranella looked, she saw rows of tiny green shoots.

If only I hadn't lost Grandmother's seeds, she thought, flowers would be sprouting now, too.

One warm Sunday a few weeks later, Pettranella went to help her father hitch up the ox, for this was the day they were going to visit their neighbors.

The ox cart bumped and bounced down the narrow trail over which they had traveled so many weeks before.

Suddenly her father stopped the cart and jumped down. "There's the rock where we broke the shaft," he said. "This time I will lead the ox around it."

Father compares this time to the last time.

"And there's the log I was sitting on when I lost the seeds," said Pettranella. "And look! LOOK AT ALL THOSE FLOWERS!"

There they were, blowing gently in the breeze, their bright faces turned to the sun—Grandmother's flowers.

"Oh," cried Pettranella, "I've never seen such beautiful flowers!"

Her mother's eyes were shining as she looked at them. "Just like the ones that grew in the countryside back home!" she exclaimed.

Pettranella's mother compares the new flowers to those at home.

"You can plant them beside our house," said her father, "and make a flower garden there for us to enjoy."

181

Pettranella did, and she tended it carefully, and so her promise to her grandmother was not broken after all.

But she left some to grow beside the trail, that other settlers might see them and not feel lonely. To this very day, Pettranella's flowers bloom each year beside a country road in Wisconsin.

A Reader Says

It turned out to be a good thing that Pettranella lost her seeds. Now she has two gardens!

How did you feel about the story?

After You Read

Thinking About What You Read

1. Why did Pettranella's family leave their home and move to a new country?

2. How did the grandmother feel about her family leaving?

3. Why were the flower seeds so important to Pettranella?

4. How did losing the seeds turn out to be fortunate after all?

Thinking About How You Read

How did comparing the way Pettranella felt when she lost the seeds with the way she felt at the end of the story help you understand the ending?

Sharing and Listening

Pettranella tells about homesteading long ago. It also tells the story of Pettranella's garden. Tell which part of the story interested you most. Why? Who or what in the story would you like to know more about? Listen as other people tell what they liked about the story.

Writing

Write a letter from Pettranella to her grandmother. Write a few sentences telling how you kept your promise to make a garden.

In other times, cowboys moved their cattle from place to place on long trail drives. Old Blue is a special steer who knows how to lead the rest of the herd.

Old Blue

by Sibyl Hancock

"Wake up, boy!" Cookie called.

Davy opened his eyes. Cookie was standing over him. "I'll be right there," Davy said. He pushed aside his blanket and folded it to make a bedroll.

The cowboys sleeping in a circle around the campfire would soon wake up hungry for breakfast. And the cowboys riding in from watching the cattle all night would be hungry, too.

A big longhorn steer, with a hide so black it looked blue, lumbered up to Davy and nudged his hand.

"Old Blue," Davy said softly, "are you hungry too?" Old Blue grunted and shook his widespread

184

horns. Davy laughed. "You think you're better than all those other longhorns. Who ever heard of a big old steer sleeping around the campfire with the cowboys!"

He rubbed Old Blue's shiny forehead. "You're a smart old steer. Not many ranchers own a steer who can lead all the rest of the cattle on a trail drive."

Davy hurried over to the chuck wagon to help Cookie. He was frying bacon in a black skillet over the fire. "Pa said I can ride today!" Davy exclaimed.

"Huh! Guess you'll feel like a real big shot!" Cookie said.

Davy smiled. He would be riding up front with the cowboys who guided the longhorn cattle over the trail. And if Pa said it was okay for him to ride, then it was, because Pa was the trail boss.

"You're a lucky boy. Not many young fellows get a chance to go on a trail ride," Cookie told him.

"If Ma hadn't gone to take care of Aunt Clara's new baby, I could never have come," Davy said.

"You can learn plenty on the trail," Cookie said.

"But right now there's plenty to do here. Let's get to work!" He handed Davy some tin plates to set out.

"Come and get it!" Cookie yelled.

While the cowboys crowded around the chuck wagon, Davy finished his breakfast. He took a handful of food scraps to Old Blue. The big steer was still eating biscuits and bacon crumbs when Pa brought a horse for Davy to ride.

"Let's get moving," Pa said. "You watch what you're doing up at the front with Old Blue."

"Yes, sir," Davy said.

"Feeling a little shaky?" Pa asked.

Davy nodded.

"I felt the same way on my first trail drive," Pa said. "You'll be fine."

Davy put on his hat. He climbed onto the horse and followed Old Blue up to the head of the herd.

One of the cowboys gave the old Texas call, "Ho, cattle, ho, ho, ho, ho!" Soon all the steers were strung in a line a mile long behind Old Blue. There were over a thousand of them.

Davy watched Old Blue walk steadily to the north. No one understood how Old Blue knew which way to go.

Sometimes Old Blue walked too fast, and the lead cowboys, or point men, had to slow him down.

"I don't like the looks of the sky," one of the cowboys said. "It could be a storm."

Davy shivered. A storm might bring icy weather, and they had a long way to go.

They had left the Goodnight Ranch in Palo Duro Canyon, Texas, a week ago. It would take two months to bring the herd into Dodge City, Kansas. There the longhorns would be shipped on railroad cars to Chicago.

Davy guided his horse past tumbleweeds rolling slowly in the breeze. Sand crunched under hooves and rose in little gold clouds.

Cattle often tried to stop and eat dry clumps of grass. And when they wandered into low mesquite trees, the cowboys had to drive them back to the herd.

Davy looked at the big steer. "Old Blue, you've got your work cut out for you. Here comes the river, and we have to cross it before the wind turns."

The water was icy, but Old Blue plunged right into it. Cattle and cowboys followed.

"Ho, cattle, ho, ho, ho, ho!" Davy yelled. The cold water splashed onto Davy's face. His horse stumbled, and Davy held on tightly.

"Keep going," he said. "Don't fall!" His horse began to swim. It seemed like a long time before they reached the other side of the river.

As the cattle came out of the chilly water, they started running to get warm. The hooves of the longhorns pounded the dusty ground.

"Let them run!" Pa shouted.

Old Blue would slow them down soon.

By late afternoon the sky grew dark. Streaks of
lightning flashed, and thunder boomed. There was
another sound, too. Horns rattled together, and
hooves pounded the dirt.

"Stampede!" Pa cried. "Get out of the way,
Davy!" he yelled.

Davy rode his horse away from the frightened
steers. He watched the cowboys guide Old Blue
around in a circle. The cattle followed. Soon most
of the herd were running in a big circle. That was
called milling. It was the only way to stop a
stampede.

"Whoa, boy!" Davy cried, trying to calm his
horse.

191

The air was full of electricity. Davy could see sparks dancing along the brim of his hat and on the tips of his horse's ears. Pa had called it *foxfire*. It even sparked from horn tip to horn tip over the milling cattle. As soon as the herd had settled down, Davy rode back to camp.

Cookie was at the chuck wagon building a fire.

"Get your slicker on," Cookie said. "It's going to be a bad night."

Davy put on his slicker and ate some cold biscuits and beans. He drank hot coffee to get warm.

"The wind is cold," Davy said.

Pa rode up to the chuck wagon. "We'll need every man in the saddle tonight," he said. "We can't let those longhorns stampede again."

"Do you want me to ride?" Davy asked.

Pa nodded. "I can use your help."

Davy pulled his hat lower over his eyes and rode out with the other cowboys.

Late that night, the rain turned to sleet. Davy could hear someone singing to keep the cattle calm. "Whoop-ee ti yi yo, git along little dogies!"

If the longhorns stampeded in this storm, some could get lost and freeze before they were found.

It was the longest night Davy could ever remember. The sleet turned to snow, and Davy couldn't even see Old Blue.

By daylight, the worst of the storm was over. The cowboys took turns eating breakfast. Davy stood by the fire trying to get warm.

"You okay, Davy?" Pa asked.

"Just cold," Davy said.

"Do you want to ride in the wagon with
Cookie?" Pa asked him.

Davy shook his head. "No, sir."

"Good boy, Davy. Cookie, how do you ever
keep a fire going in all this snow?"

"That's my secret," Cookie said.

"Hey, look who's here," Davy said.

Old Blue came close for a bit of Davy's biscuit.
"Old Blue, I almost lost you last night," Davy said,
rubbing the steer between his horns.

"When we get to Kansas City, I'm going to buy
you a big bell to wear around your neck. Then I'll
always know where you are," Davy said. "And so
will the cattle."

"No one has ever put a bell on a lead steer," Pa said, "but no steer was ever as tame as Old Blue. It's a good idea if it works."

"Davy, you don't have to wait until Kansas City. I've got a bell in the chuck wagon you can use," Cookie said. "I'll get it." He came back with a brass bell and a piece of rope.

Davy tied the bell around Old Blue's neck. "There you go, Old Blue. How do you like that?"

Old Blue shook his horns and listened to the bell clang.

"Just look how proud that old steer is," said Pa, laughing.

Davy gave Old Blue a hug. Old Blue shook his horns again and rang the bell louder than before.

If a longhorn could smile, Old Blue would have.

A Reader Says

I don't think Old Blue likes wearing a bell. He was probably shaking his horns to get the bell off.

How did you feel about the story?

After You Read

Thinking About What You Read

1. How did Davy feel about Old Blue?

2. Why did Pa let Davy ride at the front of the herd, even though it was the first time he had gone on a cattle drive?

3. Why did Davy tell Old Blue he had to lead the herd across the river before the snow storm?

4. How did Davy feel on the night of the snow storm? After that night?

Thinking About How You Read

How did comparing Davy's feelings with the way you might have felt in Davy's place help you understand the story?

Sharing and Listening

Tell what you thought was interesting about the time and life of the cowboy. Tell if you would like to have gone on a trail drive. Listen carefully as other people tell what they thought was interesting about that time.

Writing

Imagine you are Davy. Write some sentences in your diary. Write about the events of the trail drive. Write about Old Blue's new bell.

STRATEGY
◄BUILDER►

for **Memory
Poems** and
**Dinosaur
Poems**

Understanding Poetry

Starting with What You Know

In some of the things that you read and hear, the words make a pattern. The pattern may be made up of words that end with the same sounds or words that begin with the same sounds. The words may help you imagine a special person, place, thing, idea, or feeling. Tell about something you have read or heard that uses words in a pattern.

Thinking About Poetry

Writing that uses words in patterns is called **poetry**. An example of this kind of writing is the **poem** "People." Most poems have these parts:

Subject: This is what the poem is about. A poem can be about anything; for instance, an animal, friends, or a feeling, like joy.

Pattern: This is the way the words are put together. Some of the words may sound alike in some ways.

Purpose: This is why the writer wrote the poem. It might be to help you imagine something special or to describe something. It might be to tell a story, make you laugh, or make you feel a special feeling.

You can tell a poem when you see one. It does not fill up the page the way other writing does. When you read it out loud, a poem also sounds different from other writing.

Before You Read

Plan to enjoy the poem as you read it. You may want to read it out loud. Listen to the pattern of the words as you read the poem out loud. Sometimes you may want to slow down and read parts of the poem again.

As You Read

Think carefully about what the words express. Use your imagination to see and feel everything the poem is saying. Ask yourself these questions as you read:

Subject: ◆ What are my own ideas and feelings about this subject?

Pattern: ◆ In what ways do the words sound alike?

Purpose: ◆ Why did the writer write this poem?

Apply what you know about reading poetry as you read the poems that follow. Use the side notes to help you.

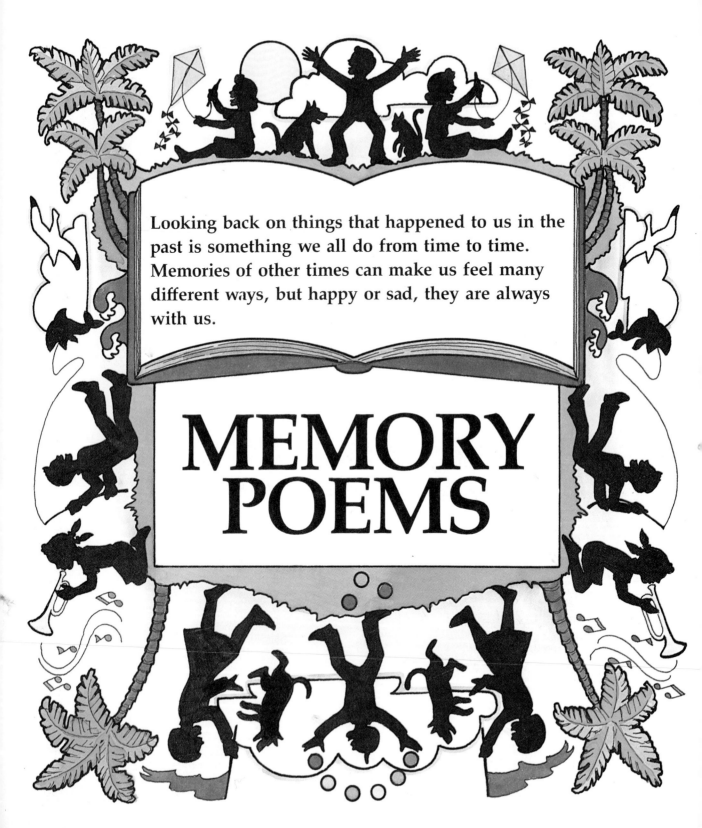

Looking back on things that happened to us in the past is something we all do from time to time. Memories of other times can make us feel many different ways, but happy or sad, they are always with us.

MEMORY POEMS

MEMORY

Memory is a tape recorder
And there's one in every head
Storing everything we've ever seen,
Or felt, or heard, or said.
The word, *remember*, simply means
We're playing back a part
Of all that's been recorded there
And lives close to our heart.
Sad thing, sweet thing,
Whatever it be,
The calling it back is a
Memory.

Mary O'Neill

This is the subject.
Some words such as *head* and *said* end with the same sounds. They come at the end of every other line.

Think about how the poem makes you feel.

GROWING UP

There are words that sound alike. Think about how often they are used.

When I was seven
We went for a picnic
Up to a magic
Foresty place.
I knew there were tigers
Behind every boulder,
Though I didn't meet one
Face to face.
When I was older
We went for a picnic
Up to the very same
Place as before,
And all of the trees
And the rocks were so little

Think about how you have grown.

They couldn't hide tigers
Or *me* anymore.

Harry Behn

A Reader Says

The boy in the forest should go back again when he is grown up. Then he would really be surprised!

How did you feel about the poems?

After You Read

Thinking About What You Read

1. What is similar about the two poems? What is different?
2. Look at the poem "Growing Up." Why did the boy think there were tigers behind every boulder when he was seven?
3. Why was the boy's memory of the forest different from how he saw it when he was older?
4. What might the boy's memory of the forest have been if he hadn't visited it again after he was seven?

Thinking About How You Read

How did looking for rhymes help you understand and enjoy the poems?

Sharing and Listening

Tell how you think memories make us feel about our own "other times." Tell if you think memories can be different from what really happened. Why? Listen carefully as other people tell what they think about memories.

Writing

How might a child remember the first circus he or she ever saw? Was the child scared? Happy? Write a story or a poem about the memory. Use the title "Remembering the Circus."

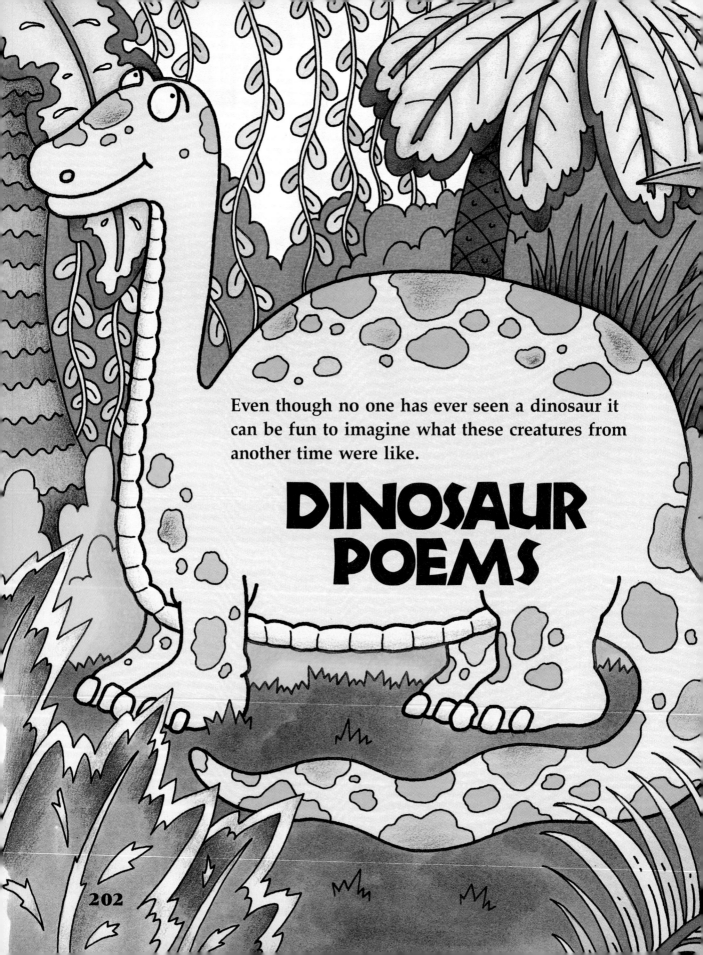

Even though no one has ever seen a dinosaur it can be fun to imagine what these creatures from another time were like.

DINOSAUR POEMS

LONG GONE

Don't waste your time in looking for
the long-extinct tyrannosaur,
because this ancient dinosaur
just can't be found here anymore.

This also goes for stegosaurus,
allosaurus, brontosaurus
and any other saur or saurus.
They all lived here long before us.

Jack Prelutsky

THE MUSEUM

I went to the museum,
it was filled with things to see,
there were rocks and gems and fossils
and a stuffed menagerie.

There were arrowheads and armor
and a mummy in a tomb,
I even saw a great blue whale
that took up one whole room.

I liked my afternoon there,
but I would have liked it more
if only they had let me pet
just one small dinosaur.

Jack Prelutsky

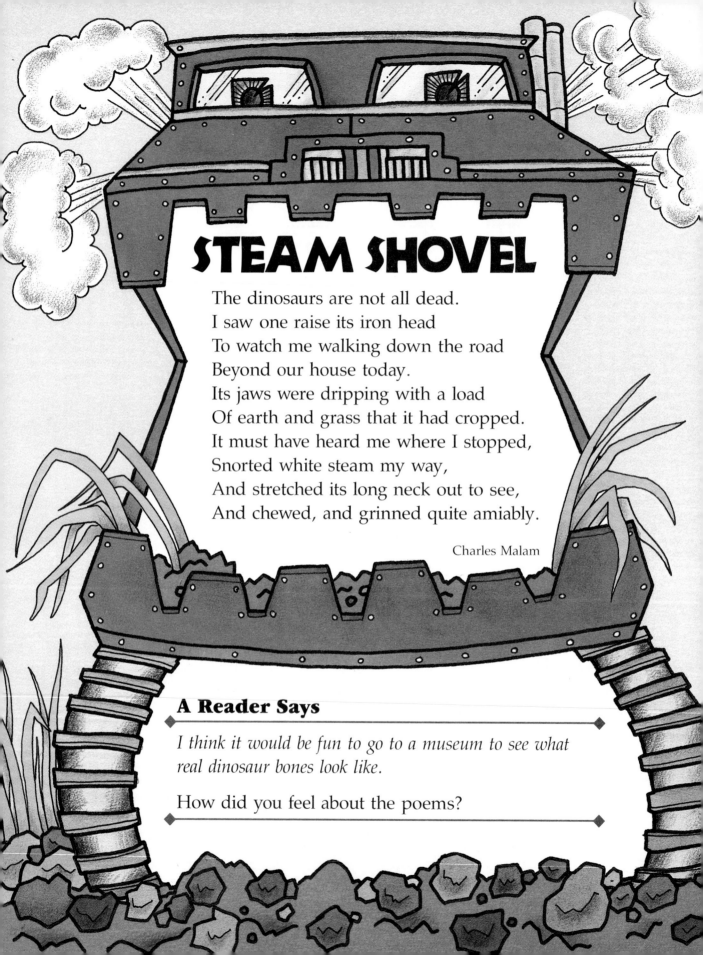

STEAM SHOVEL

The dinosaurs are not all dead.
I saw one raise its iron head
To watch me walking down the road
Beyond our house today.
Its jaws were dripping with a load
Of earth and grass that it had cropped.
It must have heard me where I stopped,
Snorted white steam my way,
And stretched its long neck out to see,
And chewed, and grinned quite amiably.

Charles Malam

A Reader Says

I think it would be fun to go to a museum to see what real dinosaur bones look like.

How did you feel about the poems?

After You Read

Thinking About What You Read

1. Why might a steam shovel have reminded the author of "Steam Shovel" of a dinosaur?

2. Why did the author of "Steam Shovel" say that "not all dinosaurs are dead"?

3. What makes you think the poem "Long Gone" was not written to give people practical information?

4. How did the author of "The Museum" feel about dinosaurs?

Thinking About How You Read

How did knowing that "The Museum" was a poem and not a story help you read the sentences?

Sharing and Listening

Each of the three poems talks about dinosaurs. Tell how you thought the poems were alike. How were they different? Then tell which of the poems you enjoyed the most. Why? Listen as other people give their ideas about the poems.

Writing

Write a few sentences telling why many people are interested in dinosaurs. Has anyone ever seen one? Why is it fun to imagine what the world was like during the time of the dinosaurs?

Memories of other times in our lives are very important and special. The woman telling this story remembers her childhood as a time of warmth and love.

IN COAL COUNTRY

◆

by Judith Hendershot

Papa dug coal from deep in the earth to earn a living. He dressed for work when everyone else went to bed. He wore faded denims and steel-toed shoes and he walked a mile to his job at the mine every night. He carried a silver lunch bucket and had a light on his miner's hat. It was important work. He was proud to do it.

In the morning I listened for the whistle that signaled the end of the hoot-owl shift. Sometimes I walked up the run to meet Papa. He was always covered with grime and dirt, but I could see the whites of his eyes smiling at me. He let me carry his silver lunch bucket.

208

When we got home, Mama took the number three tub from where it hung on the back porch and filled it with water heated on the huge iron stove. She draped a blanket across one corner of the kitchen, and Papa washed off the coal dust. We got a bath only on Saturdays, but Papa had one every day. Then Papa went to bed and we went to school.

We lived in a place called the Company Row. The ten white houses sat in a straight line. They were built by the people who owned the Black Diamond Mine. Two miners' families lived side by side in each two-story house. Seventy-five children lived and played there in the row. We had many friends.

Outside, our houses never looked clean or painted. Coal was burned in the furnaces to heat the houses and in the stoves to cook the food. The stove fires sent smoke and soot up the chimneys. The smoke had a disagreeable smell, and something in it made the paint peel off the houses. Tiny specks of soot floated out and covered everything.

Our coal camp was called Willow Grove. The houses were huddled in a hollow between two softly rising hills. In the spring the hills were covered with lady's-slippers and yellow and white violets. Mama always had a jar of spring flowers on the kitchen table. Weeping willow trees lined the banks of the creek that flowed behind the Company Row.

The water in the creek was often black. The coal was dragged out of the mine in small cars pulled by mules.   Then it was sent up into a tall building called the tipple, where it was sorted and washed. The water that washed the coal ran into the creek, and the dust from the coal turned it black as night.

Papa sometimes worked at the picking table on the tipple to sort out rocks from the good coal. After it was sorted, the good coal was dumped into railroad cars waiting under the tipple. The rest of the stone and dirt was hauled away to a gob pile. There were gob piles all over Willow Grove. The kids from the row ran to the tops of the piles to play king of the mountain.

Sometimes a gob pile caught fire. It smoldered for a long time, maybe for days, and it smelled awful. When the fire went out, the stone and ash that was left was called red dog. Our roads were made of the sharp red-dog stone.

Trains moved the coal in cars from the mine to power plants and steel mills on the Ohio River. The train tracks ran alongside the Company Row. We watched from the porch swing as the engineer worked his levers to guide the train, blowing clouds of hot white steam on the tracks. One engine pushed and another pulled as many as one hundred cars at a time. The houses shook as the trains rumbled by.

The coal cars moved all through the day and into the night. Sometimes in the middle of the night we heard the clang of steel as the cars were hitched to the engine. Often the load was too much for the engine. It groaned. The tracks creaked. The wheels screeched as the brakeman spread sand on the rails to get the cars moving. Then the train began to move very slowly, and we could hear the wheels straining a slow "Chug-a-chug, chug-a-chug." Later, in the distance, the engine's whistle moaned a familiar cry. "Whoo-whoo."

In the morning we took buckets and gathered the lumps of coal that had rolled off the cars in the struggle the night before.

The vibration of the trains often made the rails on the tracks come apart. When that happened, the paddy man came to repair the tracks. He rode a flatcar, which he pedaled by himself. While he worked to replace the spikes in the rails, the paddy man sang:

> *"Paddy on the railroad,*
> *Paddy on the sea.*
> *Paddy ripped his pants,*
> *And he blamed it on me."*

Mama worked hard like Papa. She planted our garden and she canned vegetables for the winter. She stored her quart jars of beans and tomatoes and peas in the earthen room in the cellar. Every other day Mama baked her special rye bread in the oven of the iron stove. We often ate the bread right out of the oven with fried potatoes and sliced tomatoes.

Washing the clothes was a long, hard job. We carried the wash water from the pump down by the creek. Mama heated the water in a copper boiler on her huge stove. She scrubbed the clothes on a washboard with a stiff brush. Her hands were red and wrinkled when she was finished.

In the summer, when it was hot, the Company Row kids often climbed the hills above the grove. We cooled ourselves by standing under Bernice Falls. The water flowed from a natural spring on the ridge above. It was cool and clean and it tasted so sweet.

We walked the red-dog road to the Company Store. Anything the miners' families needed, from matches to pongee dresses, could be found there. Every payday Papa treated us to an Eskimo Pie.

The Company Row kids played hopscotch in the dirt. Our favorite game was mumbletypeg. In the evenings we built bonfires along the creek and roasted potatoes on willow sticks.

In the autumn the hills were ablaze with color. We gathered hickory nuts and butternuts and dragged them home in burlap sacks. Papa shelled them and spread them on the porch roof to dry. Mama used the nutmeats in cookies at holiday time.

In the winter we climbed from the hollow to Baker's Ridge. Our sleds were made from leftover tin used for roofs, and we rode them down through the woods by moonlight. When the black creek was frozen, we shared a few skates and everyone took a turn. When we got home, we hung our wet clothes over the stove to dry and warmed ourselves in Mama's kitchen.

Christmas in the row was the best time of the year. Papa cut a fresh tree up on the ridge, and we pulled it home on a tin sled. Mama placed a candle on the end of each branch. The tree was lighted once, on Christmas Eve. Papa spent the whole day basting the roast goose for Mama. Our stockings bulged with tangerines and nuts and hard cinnamon candies. The house smelled of Christmas tree and roast goose and all the good things that Mama had made. No whistle called Papa to the mine. Everything felt so special. And it was.

A Reader Says

I would like it if my Dad worked at night instead of during the day. He could sleep while I was at school and be ready to play when I got home.

How did you feel about the story?

218

About the Author

Judith Hendershot

Judith Hendershot was born and grew up in Ohio. Her father and both of her grandfathers worked in a coal mine. Her parents often told her stories about growing up in coal country. She uses those stories and her own memories when she writes.

In Coal Country is Mrs. Hendershot's first book. Her story shows what growing up in a small coal-mining town was like in the 1930s. It was a life filled with excitement and hard work. Everyone in that little world was touched in some way by the coal mine. "It was important work," Mrs. Hendershot wrote. "My father was proud to do it."

Mrs. Hendershot now teaches school in a small Ohio town. She and her husband have three grown children and one grandchild.

The Ohio coal country has changed a lot since Mrs. Hendershot was a girl. The way of life she tells about has disappeared. Still, the story makes the past come alive again.

More Books About Other Times ◆

If You Are a Hunter of Fossils
by Byrd Baylor
Dinosaurs weren't the only animals who lived millions of years ago. *If You Are a Hunter of Fossils* tells you about many creatures of other times, and how you might find traces of them today.

Little House in the Big Woods
by Laura Ingalls Wilder
Laura Ingalls Wilder has written many books about what it was like to be growing up in frontier America. In *Little House in the Big Woods*, her first book, she tells about her years spent in the woods of Wisconsin.

Ox-Cart Man
by Donald Hall, illustrated by Barbara Cooney
In this book you'll read about the very early days of our country. Each member of a New England family works all winter to make something for the father to sell at market in the spring.

The Sheriff of Rottenshot
by Jack Prelutsky
Did you enjoy Jack Prelutsky's poems? If so, read this book and meet his funny characters from past and present.

MAKING ALL THE
CONNECTIONS

Speaking and Listening

In this part of the book, you read about other times. Some of the stories were about how people feel about other times. Other stories told about what life was like in these times. You read about how Dudley learns why people are curious about other times. You read how Pettranella brings something from another time in her life to share in her new life. You read poems about memories of other times and creatures from other times. You also read about one girl's memories of coal country.

Discuss the stories you read with your classmates. You may want to look back at your Reader's Log. Speak clearly when you give your thoughts. Listen carefully as others share their thoughts with you. Here are some questions to help you.

1. What other times did you read about in the stories?
2. Talk about a time that is interesting to you. What would you do if you lived in that time?
3. Think of your own life. What things that you know about life today might be interesting to people from another time? What things about life today do you want to remember?

Thinking About Another Time

In this part of the book, you have also read about memories of other times. Now you are going to make some memories of your own in a way that people did long ago, and some people still do today. You are going to make a patchwork quilt.

In other times, people would save pieces of material and sew them into squares. Then they would sew the squares together to make a quilt.

One piece of cloth might be from a jacket worn the first day of school, another piece might be from a wedding dress, and still another piece might be from a baby's first blanket. When they were all put together, the quilt would be made up of memories of those times.

The designs of some quilts were also collections of memories. The quiltmaker might design a bird that was seen on a special day into the quilt. A house might appear in one patch. The flower garden might be sewn into the design.

These wonderful quilts were passed on from parents to their children and then to their children's children. Maybe you have a family quilt in your house.

The quilt that you are going to make will not be of cloth. Your quilt will be made out of paper. It will be a quilt to help you remember your days in school.

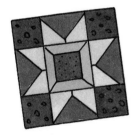   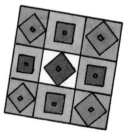

Making a Memory Quilt

Work with three other classmates. You will need paper, scissors, magazines, glue, crayons, and tape. Before you start making your quilt, you will have to come up with a plan. Here are some things you can talk about.

- Each of you pick a school memory that you want to be part of your quilt.
- Decide who is going to make that square.
- Decide what colors you want to use.

After you have talked about your quilt, it is time to begin making it. Follow these steps.

1. Each person will have one piece of paper. That paper is your quilt square.

2. The squares must each be the same size. It is up to your group to choose the size.

3. Draw your design on your square. Then color it with the crayons. If you do not wish to draw a design, you can cut out pictures from the magazines and paste them on your square.

4. When all of the squares are finished, decide how you want to put them together. Try out several ways and decide which you like best.

5. Finally, paste the squares together with tape. Be sure to tape the back of the quilt. You do not want tape on the front, or the side with the pictures.

   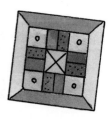

Presenting Your Memory Quilt

Now that you have finished your quilt, it is time to share it with the other groups. Here are some ways that you can do this.

Tell a quilt story: Each group can display its quilt to the class. Point to the square that you made. Tell what memory it stands for. Then tell why you chose that memory to draw. Remember to speak slowly and clearly when you are telling about your square. Listen carefully while other classmates tell about their memory squares.

Make a quilt scrapbook: Each group can paste its memory quilt onto a piece of heavy construction paper. Write a sentence telling what each square stands for. Then put all of the quilts together in a book. You can keep the book in your classroom and it will always be there to remind you of the memories you drew and saved.

Make a giant classroom quilt: Put all of the quilts together to make one big quilt. Display the quilt on the classroom bulletin board.

PART FOUR

Other Places

Now mix me a color that nobody knows,
And paint me a country where nobody goes.
And put in it people a little like you,
Watching a unicorn drinking the dew.

from *The Paint Box*
by E.V. Rieu

◆

Visiting a place you've never been before can be
very exciting. You never know what will happen!
The people and animals you'll read about in this
section are all on journeys to new places. As you
read, think: What will you find when you visit
other places?

227

Exploring Words About Other Places

Starting with What You Know

When you think of other places, what ideas come to mind? The words in the box below tell about other places. Use these words and words of your own to answer the questions after the box.

travel	colorful	far away
beautiful	country	magical
sail	island	city

Some people might say other places are beautiful. How would you describe other places? Another place might be a village. What else might another place be? One way to travel to a place is to drive. What other ways can you travel to a place?

Building a Word Map

The word map shows how some of the words in the box above go together. Think about words you can add to the map. Use words from the box and other words of your own.

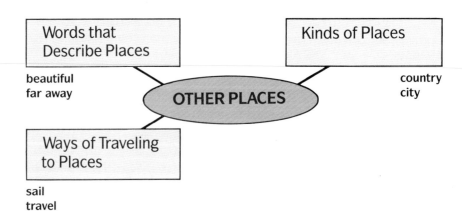

Words that Describe Places
beautiful
far away

Kinds of Places
country
city

OTHER PLACES

Ways of Traveling to Places
sail
travel

Finishing a Story

Look at the story below. The story tells about other places. Some words are missing. Think of the words you would use to finish the story.

Use the words from the box and word map in this lesson for ideas. Complete the story.

Rene and Juan are planning a _____. Rene wants to go to a _____ place. Juan wants to go to a _____ place. Finally, they both agree to visit a small _____.

"Let's fly there on a _____," says Juan.
"No, let's _____ there on a _____," says Rene.
The two decide to _____ to the place. What will happen on their journey? Will they meet _____ people? Will they see _____ things?

Share your story with your classmates. How were the stories different? What words did your classmates use?

As You Read

In this part of the book, you will read about exciting places. Keeping a Reader's Log will help you remember important thoughts, ideas, and words. As you read, make notes in your log. You could begin your Reader's Log with the word map. Add new words to the map as you find them.

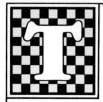

Any place can seem strange if you're not sure what to expect. In this story, the ocean suddenly becomes out of the ordinary to two creatures who make it their home.

THE **L**OBSTER **AND THE C**RAB

♦

by Arnold Lobel

On a stormy day, the Crab went strolling along the beach. He was surprised to see the Lobster preparing to set sail in her boat.

"Lobster," said the Crab, "it is foolish to go out on a day like this."

"Perhaps so," she replied, "but I love a squall at sea!"

"I will come with you," said the Crab. "I will not let you face such danger alone."

The Lobster and the Crab began their voyage. Soon they found themselves far from shore. Their boat was tossed and buffeted by the stormy seas.

"Crab!" shouted the Lobster above the roar of the wind. "For me, the splashing of the salt spray is thrilling! The crashing of every wave takes my breath away!"

"Lobster, I think we are sinking!" cried the Crab.

"Yes, of course, we are sinking," said the Lobster. "This old boat is full of holes. Have courage, my friend. Remember, we are both creatures of the sea."

The little boat tipped over and sank.

"Horrors!" cried the Crab.

"Down we go!" shouted the Lobster.

The Crab was shaken and upset. The Lobster took him for a relaxing walk along the ocean floor.

"How brave we are," said the Lobster. "What a wonderful adventure we have had!"

The Crab began to feel somewhat better. Although he usually led a quieter life, he had to admit that the day had been pleasantly out of the ordinary.

Even the taking of small risks will add excitement to life.

Thinking About the Theme

1. Was going out in the boat on a stormy day a dangerous thing for the Lobster and the Crab to do?

2. The last line of the story tells us how the author feels about going to other places or trying new things. Do you agree or disagree with him?

Drawing Conclusions

Starting with What You Know

How would you describe what has happened in the picture? What clues helped you?

Thinking About Conclusions

Sometimes a writer does not describe everything that happens in a story. Sometimes the writer gives you clues, and you **draw a conclusion**. Read the following description. What conclusion can you draw?

> Annette walked slowly into the garage. She had a sad look on her face. She put her fishing rod and bait bucket in the corner. She didn't know what had gone wrong. Maybe she would catch something tomorrow.

The story doesn't say that Annette didn't catch any fish. But there are clues that help you draw that conclusion.

Practice

Read each paragraph, and draw a conclusion that answers the questions. Tell which clues helped you draw your conclusion.

When her parents told her it was safe, Angela opened the window. As she looked out, she saw that one of the electricity cables to the house was lying on the grass. Here and there some broken tree branches also lay on the wet lawn. The wind was still blowing strong, but the sky was clearing.

What has happened?

A large clock on the wall showed that it was two o'clock in the afternoon. On another wall, there was a list of cities and times, telling when trains were leaving or arriving. Hundreds of people were walking in and out of large doorways. Some people were carrying suitcases. Every now and then Curtis heard a loud voice say "All aboard."

Where is Curtis?

As You Read

Drawing conclusions helps you understand more of what has happened in a story. Ask yourself these questions:

◆ What clues are there?
◆ What do I already know that helps me draw a conclusion?

Apply what you know about drawing conclusions as you read the two selections that follow. Use the side notes to help you.

Sometimes there are exciting places not far from home. Eva has been going to an unusual place all her life, but today is the first time she will go alone.

Very Last

ΛVΛVΛVΛVΛVΛVΛVΛVΛVΛVΛVΛVΛVΛVΛVΛVΛVΛVΛVΛVΛVΛVΛVΛ

First Time

by Jan Andrews

Eva Padlyat lived in a village on Ungava Bay in northern Canada. She was Inuit, and ever since she could remember she had walked with her mother on the bottom of the sea. It was something the people of her village did in winter when they wanted mussels to eat.

Today, something very special was going to happen. Today, for the very first time in her life, Eva would walk on the bottom of the sea alone.

Eva got ready. Standing in their small, warm kitchen, Eva looked at her mother and smiled.

"Shall we go now?"

"I think we'd better."

"We'll start out together, won't we?"

Eva's mother nodded. Pulling up their warm hoods, they went out.

Think about how people could walk safely on the bottom of the sea.

Think about how Eva feels.

236

Beside the house there were two sleds, each holding a shovel, a long ice-chisel, and a mussel pan. Dragging the sleds behind them, they started off.

Eva and her mother walked through the village. Snow lay white as far as the eye could see—snow, but not a single tree, for miles and miles on the vast northern tundra. The village was off by itself. There were no highways, but snowmobile tracks led away and disappeared into the distance.

Their village seems far away.

237

Down by the shore they met some friends and stopped for a quick greeting.

They had come at the right time. The tide was out, pulling the sea water away, so there would be room for them to climb under the thick ice and wander about on the seabed.

Eva and her mother walked carefully over the bumps and ridges of the frozen sea. Soon they found a spot where the ice was cracked and broken.

"This is the right place," Eva said.

After shoveling away a pile of snow, she reached for the ice-chisel. She worked it under an ice hump and, heaving and pushing with her mother's help, made a hole.

Think about what Eva already knows.

Eva peered down into the hole and felt the
dampness of the air below. She breathed deep to
catch the salt sea smell.

"Good luck," Eva's mother said.

Eva grinned. "Good luck yourself."

Her eyes lit up with excitement and she threw
her mussel pan into the hole. Then she lowered
herself slowly into the darkness, feeling with her
feet until they touched a rock and she could let go
of the ice above.

In a minute, she was standing on the seabed.

Above her, in the ice hole, the wind whistled.
Eva struck a match and lit a candle. The gold-bright
flame shone and glistened on the wet stones and
pools at her feet.

Think about how
cold it must be if
the ice is so thick.

239

She held her candle and saw strange shadow shapes around her. The shadows formed a wolf, a bear, a seal sea-monster. Eva watched them, then she remembered.

"I'd better get to work," she said.

Lighting three more candles, she carefully wedged them between stones so she could see to collect mussels. Using her knife as a lever, she tugged and pried and scraped to pull the mussels off the rocks. She was in luck. There were strings of blue-black mussel shells whichever way she turned.

Alone—for the first time.

Eva was so happy she started to sing. Her song echoed around, so she sang louder. She hummed far back in her throat to make the echoes rumble. She lifted up long strings of mussels and let them clatter into her pan.

Soon her mussel pan was full, so she had time to explore.

Imagine what the space was like under the ice.

She found a rock pool that was deep and clear.
Small shrimps in the water darted and skittered in
the light from her candle. She stopped to watch
them. Reaching under a ledge, she touched a
pinky-purple crab. The fronds of the anemones on
the ledge tickled her wrist.

Beyond the rock pool, seaweed was piled in
thick, wet, shiny heaps and masses. Eva scrambled
over the seaweed, up and onto a rock mound.
Stretching her arms wide, tilting her head back, she
laughed, imagining the shifting, waving, lifting
swirl of seaweed when the tide comes in.

The tide!

Eva listened. The lap, lap of the waves sounded
louder and nearer. Whoosh and roar and whoosh
again.

Guess what will
happen next.

241

Eva jumped off the rock, stumbled—and her candle dropped and sputtered out. She had gone too far. The candles she had set down between the stones had burned to nothing. There was darkness—darkness all around.

"Help me!" she called, but her voice was swallowed. "Someone come quickly."

Eva closed her eyes. Her hands went to her face. She could not bear to look.

She felt in her pockets. She knew she had more candles there, but she could not seem to find them.

The tide was roaring louder and the ice shrieked and creaked with its movement.

Eva's hands groped deeper. She took a candle out at last and her box of matches, but her fingers were shaking and clumsy. For a long, forever moment, she could not strike the match to light the candle.

Think about how Eva feels now.

Think about why Eva is afraid.

242

The flame seemed pale and weak.

Eva walked slowly, fearfully, peering through the shadows, looking for her mussel pan.

At last, she found it and ran stumbling to the ice-hole. Then, looking up, Eva saw the moon in the sky. It was high and round and big. Its light cast a circle through the hole onto the seabed at her feet.

Eva stood in the moonlight. Her parka glowed. Blowing out her candle, she slowly began to smile.

By the time her mother came, she was dancing. She was skipping and leaping in and out of the moonglow circle, darkness and light, in and out.

"Eva," her mother called.

"I'm here," she called back. "Take my mussel pan."

Notice the clues as to what time of day it is.

Eva's mood has changed. Think about the clues.

Eva scrambled onto a rock and held the pan up high to her mother. Then her mother's hands reached down and pulled her up, too, through the hole.

Squeezing her mother's hand, Eva saw the moon, shining on the snow and ice, and felt the wind on her face once more.

"That was my last very first—my very last *first* time—for walking alone on the bottom of the sea," Eva said.

A Reader Says

At first I didn't understand that Eva was not really going to be underwater, and I was worried she wouldn't be able to breathe. Still, I think that what Eva did was pretty dangerous.

How did you feel about the story?

After You Read

Thinking About What You Read

1. Why did Eva's mother let her walk on the bottom of the sea alone?

2. How did Eva's exploring get her into a dangerous situation?

3. Why didn't anyone hear Eva when she called out?

4. How did Eva feel about her first time alone under the ice after she got out?

Thinking About How You Read

How did what you know about how people feel when they do new things help you draw conclusions about Eva's feelings?

Sharing and Listening

Tell if you thought Eva was brave or foolish. Why? Tell if you think Eva will go looking for mussels again. Why or why not? Give reasons for the way you feel. Listen carefully as other people give their ideas.

Writing

Do you ever dream about a place different from anyplace you have ever been before? What is it like? Does anyone live there? Write a paragraph or more describing what life is like there.

Sometimes you hear so much about a place it seems like you've been there yourself. Adan's family and friends have told him a lot about Puerto Rico. Now it's time for him to find out if it's everything he's imagined.

Yagua Days

by Cruz Martel

It was drizzling steadily on the Lower East Side. From the doorway of his parents' *bodega*[1], Adan Riera watched a car splash the sidewalk.

School had ended for the summer two days ago, and for two days it had rained. Adan wanted to play in East River Park, but with so much rain about the only thing a boy could do was watch cars splash by.

Of course he could help father. Adan enjoyed working in the bodega. He liked the smells of the fruits and the different colors of the vegetables, and he liked the way the mangos and *quenepas* felt in his hands.

But today he would rather be in the park. He watched another car spray past. The rain began to fall harder.

[1]For the meanings and pronunciations of Spanish words, see the word list on pages 257-258.

246

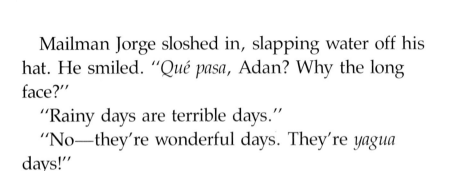

Mailman Jorge sloshed in, slapping water off his hat. He smiled. "*Qué pasa*, Adan? Why the long face?"

"Rainy days are terrible days."

"No—they're wonderful days. They're *yagua* days!"

"Stop teasing, Jorge. Yesterday you told me the vegetables and fruits in the bodega are grown in panel trucks. What's a yagua day?"

"*Muchacho*, *this* day is a yagua day. And Puerto Rican vegetables and fruits *are* grown in trucks. Why, I have a truck myself. Every day I water it!"

Adan's mother and father came in from the back.

"*Hola*, Jorge. You look wet."

"I *feel* wetter. But it's a wonderful feeling. It's a yagua-day feeling!"

His mother and father liked Jorge. They had all grown up together in Puerto Rico.

"So you've been telling Adan about yagua days?"

"*Sí. Mira*! Here's a letter for you from *Corral Viejo*, where we all had some of the best yagua days."

Adan's father read the letter. "Good news! My brother Ulise wants *Mami*, Adan, and me to visit him on his *finca* for two weeks."

"You haven't been to Puerto Rico in years," said Mailman Jorge.

"Adan's *never* been there," replied his mother. "We can ask my brother to take care of the bodega. Adan will meet his family in the mountains at last."

Adan clapped his hands. "Puerto Rico! Who cares about the rain!"

Mailman Jorge smiled. "Maybe you'll even have a few yagua days. *Hasta luego. Y que gocen mucho!*"

249

Tío Ulise met them at the airport in *Ponce.*

"Welcome to Puerto Rico, Adan."

Stocky Uncle Ulise had tiny blue eyes in a round, red face, and big, strong arms, but Adan, excited after his first plane ride, hugged Uncle Ulise even harder than Uncle Ulise hugged him.

"Come, we'll drive to Corral Viejo." He winked at Adan's father. "I'm sorry you didn't arrive yesterday. Yesterday was a wonderful yagua day."

"You know about yagua days too, Tío Ulise?"

"Sure. They're my favorite days."

"But wouldn't today be a good yagua day?"

"The worst. The sun's out!"

In an old jeep, they wound up into the mountains.

"Look!" said Uncle Ulise, pointing at a river jumping rocks. "Your mother and father, Mailman Jorge, and I played in that river when we were children."

They bounced up a hill to a cluster of bright houses. Many people were outside.

"This is your family, Adan," said Uncle Ulise.

Everyone crowded around the jeep. Old and young people. Blond-, brown-, and black-haired people. Dark-skinned and light-skinned people. Blue-eyed, brown-eyed, and green-eyed people. Adan had not known there were so many people in his family.

Uncle Ulise's wife Carmen hugged Adan and kissed both his cheeks. Taller than Uncle Ulise and very thin, she carried herself like a soldier. Her straight mouth never smiled—but her eyes did.

The whole family sat under wide trees and ate rice, roast pork, and avocado and tomato salad.

Adan talked and sang until his voice turned to a squeak. He ate until his stomach almost popped a pants button.

Afterward he fell asleep under a big mosquito net before the sun had even gone down behind the mountains.

In the morning Uncle Ulise called out, "Adan, everyone ate all the food. Let's get more."

"From a bodega?"

"No, *mi amor*. From my finca on the mountain."

"You drive a tractor and plow on the mountain?"

Tía Carmen smiled with her eyes. "We don't need tractors and plows on our finca."

"I don't understand."

"*Vente*. You will."

Adan and his parents, Aunt Carmen, and Uncle Ulise hiked up the mountain beside a splashy stream.

Near the top they walked through groves of fruit trees.

"Long ago your grandfather planted these trees," Adan's mother said. "Now Aunt Carmen and Uncle Ulise pick what they need for themselves or want to give away or sell in Ponce."

"Let's work!" said Aunt Carmen.

Sitting on his father's shoulders, Adan picked oranges. Swinging a hooked stick, he pulled down mangos.

Finally, gripping a very long pole, he struck down coconuts.

"How do we get all the food down the mountain?" he asked.

"Watch," said Aunt Carmen. She whistled loudly.

Adan saw a patch of white moving in the trees. A horse with a golden mane appeared.

Uncle Ulise fed him a *guanábana*. The horse twitched his ears and munched loudly.

"Palomo will help us carry all the fruit and vegetables we've picked," Adan's mother said.

Back at the house, Adan gave Palomo another guanábana.

"He'll go back up to the finca now," his father said. "He's got all he wants to eat there."

Uncle Ulise rubbed his knee.

"*Qué te pasa*?" asked Adan's mother.

"My knee. It always hurts just before rain comes."

Adan looked at the cloudless sky. "But it's not going to rain."

253

"Yes, it will. My knee never lies. It'll rain tonight. Maybe tomorrow. Say! When it does, it'll be a yagua day!"

In the morning Adan, waking up cozy under his mosquito net, heard rain banging on the metal roof and *coquies* beeping like tiny car horns.

He jumped out of bed and got a big surprise. His mother and father, Uncle Ulise, and Aunt Carmen were on the porch wearing bathing suits.

"*Vámonos*, Adan," his father said. "It's a wonderful yagua day. Put on your bathing suit!"

In the forest he heard shouts and swishing noises in the rain.

Racing into a clearing, he saw boys and girls shooting down a runway of grass, then disappearing over a rock ledge.

Uncle Ulise picked up a canoelike object from the grass. "This is a yagua, Adan. It fell from this palm tree."

"And this is what we do with it," said his father. He ran, then belly-flopped on the yagua. He skimmed down the grass, sailed up into the air, and vanished over the ledge. His mother found another yagua and did the same.

"*Papi*! Mami!"

Uncle Ulise laughed. "Don't worry, Adan. They won't hurt themselves. The river is down there. It pools beneath the ledge. The rain turns the grass butter-slick so you can zip into the water. That's what makes it a yagua day! Come and join us!"

That day Adan found out what fun a yagua day is!

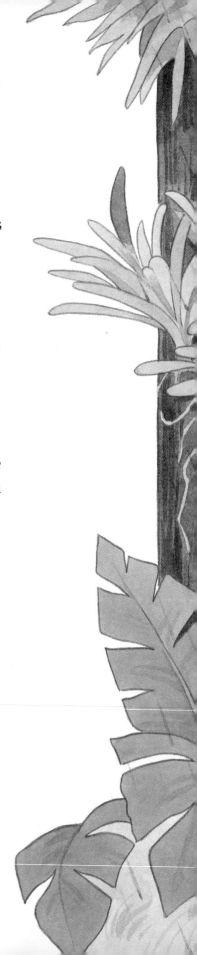

Two weeks later Adan lifted a box of mangos off the panel truck back in New York.

"Hola, muchacho! Welcome home!"

Adan smiled at Mailman Jorge. "You look sad, *compadre*."

"Too much mail! Too much sun!"

"What you need is a yagua day."

"So you know what a yagua day is?"

"I had six yagua days in Puerto Rico."

"You went over the ledge?"

"Of course."

"Into the river?"

"Sí! Sí! Into the river. Sliding on yaguas!"

"Two-wheeled or four-wheeled yaguas?"

Adan laughed. "Yaguas don't have wheels. They come from palm trees."

"I thought they came from panel trucks like mine."

"Nothing grows in trucks, Jorge. These mangos and oranges come from trees. Compadre, wake up. Don't *you* know?"

Mailman Jorge laughed. "Come, *campesino*, let's talk with your parents. I want to hear all about your visit to Corral Viejo!"

A Reader Says

I think Adan was lucky to get to go to Puerto Rico. I'd like to see the place where my parents grew up and find out about what they did when they were children.

How did you feel about the story?

Spanish Word List

bodega (bō·dā′gə), Puerto Rican grocery store.

campesino (kam·pə·sē′nō), country boy.

compadre (kom·pä′dre), pal.

coquíes (kō·kē′əs), tree frogs.

Corral Viejo (kō·rôl′ vē·ye′hō), old corral.

finca (fēn′cä), plantation.

guanábana (gwa·na′ba·na), a sweet, pulpy fruit.

hasta luego (ä′stä lü·we′ gō), till we meet again; good-bye.

hola (ō′la), hello.

mami (ma′mē), mommy.

mi amor (mē ä·mör′), my love.

mira (mē′ra), look.

257

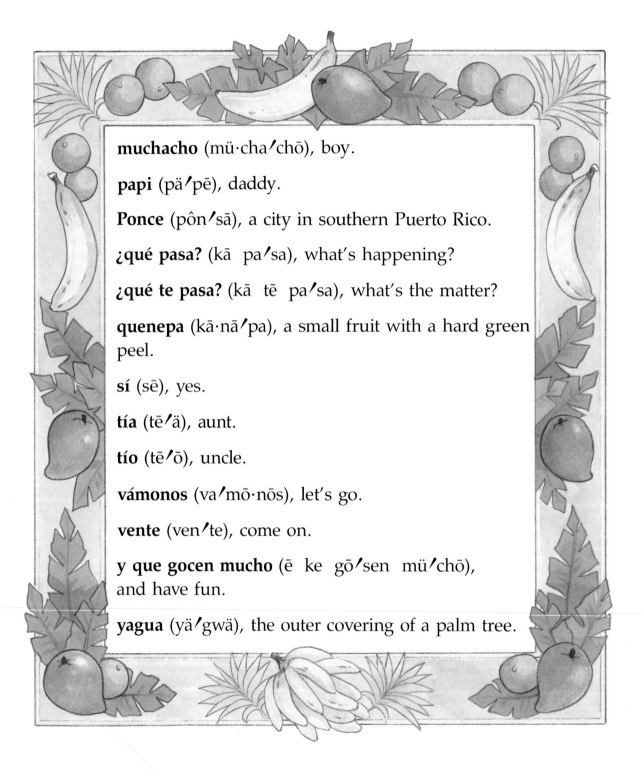

muchacho (mü·cha′chō), boy.

papi (pä′pē), daddy.

Ponce (pôn′sā), a city in southern Puerto Rico.

¿qué pasa? (kā pa′sa), what's happening?

¿qué te pasa? (kā tē pa′sa), what's the matter?

quenepa (kā·nā′pa), a small fruit with a hard green peel.

sí (sē), yes.

tía (tē′ä), aunt.

tío (tē′ō), uncle.

vámonos (va′mō·nōs), let's go.

vente (ven′te), come on.

y que gocen mucho (ē ke gō′sen mü′chō), and have fun.

yagua (yä′gwä), the outer covering of a palm tree.

258

After You Read

Thinking About What You Read

1. How did Jorge the mailman feel about Adan? Why did Jorge tease Adan so much?

2. Why didn't Jorge or Adan's parents tell him what yagua days were?

3. How might Adan's feelings about Puerto Rico have changed after he visited it?

4. How did Adan feel about experiencing yagua days?

Thinking About How You Read

How did using what you know about families help you draw conclusions about how Adan's family felt about their time together in Puerto Rico?

Sharing and Listening

Tell what you would like to know more about, Adan's life in New York or life at Uncle Ulise's house in Puerto Rico. Why? Listen carefully as other people give their opinions.

Writing

Imagine you have visited your family in the mountains of Puerto Rico. Write a letter telling about the tradition of yagua days. Compare the fun of yagua days to the fun of other sports or games.

for **The Wizard of Oz, Part One** and **Part Two**

Understanding Plays

Starting with What You Know

Sometimes people dress up and act out a story. They are putting on a **play**. What play have you seen or been in?

Thinking About a Play

A play is a story that is acted out by real people. The people who act out the play are called **actors**. A play has the same parts as a story:

Characters: These are the people or animals in the story. They have a problem or a goal.

Setting: This is the place where the story happens.

Plot: These are the important actions in the story.

Outcome: This is the way the story ends. In many stories, the main character solves a problem or reaches a goal.

The printed form of the play is called the **script**. The script names all of the characters and tells

what they say to each other. The script also tells how the characters move around during the play. Some plays have a **narrator**. The narrator acts like a storyteller and tells about the other characters and events.

Before You Read

A play looks different from a story. First, you see a character's name, and then you see what the character says. Then you see the next character's name and what that character says and so on. You will also see words that tell you how each character moves or behaves. These words may be in special print like this: (*moves to the table in front of the fireplace*). Before you read, find out who the characters are. Plan to read carefully.

As You Read

Think about what the characters say and do. Ask yourself these questions:

Characters: ◆ Who are the characters?
◆ What is their goal or problem?
◆ How do they move or behave?
Setting: ◆ Where does the action take place?
Plot: ◆ What are the important things that happen in the play?
Outcome: ◆ How does the play end?
◆ How do the characters reach their goal or solve their problem?

Apply what you know about reading plays as you read the two parts of the play that follows. Use the side notes to help you.

The Little Road

A little road was straying
  Across a little hill.
I asked, "May I go with you, Road?"
  It answered, "If you will."

'Twas travel-stained and shabby,
  And dust was on its face.
Said I: "How fine to wander free
  To every lovely place!"

"O, if you're off to mountains
  Or if you're off to sea,
Or if you're bound across the world,
  It's all the same to me."

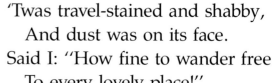

We loitered in the sunlight,
  We journeyed on together;
The sky was like a bluebird's wing,
  The wind was like a feather.

We passed a ruddy robin
   Who called, "How do you do?"
Some daisies shook their bonnets back
   And begged, "Ah, take us too!"

A squirrel briefly joined us,
   A brook came hurrying down;
We wandered through a meadow green
   And by a busy town.

When dusky twilight met us,
   No feet so slow as mine.
"Why, there's a little house," I said,
   "With windows all ashine.

"Perhaps, since night is nearing,
   I'd rather rest than roam."
"I knew you would," said Little Road;
   "That's why I brought you home."

Nancy Byrd Turner

263

Dorothy suddenly finds herself in a strange new place. What will she find in the distant Land of Oz?

The Wizard of Oz
Part One

by Lynne Sharon Schwartz

based on the classic book
by L. Frank Baum

CAST

NARRATOR	CAPTAIN
DOROTHY	OZ, the wizard
WITCH OF THE NORTH	WICKED WITCH OF
TWO MUNCHKINS	THE WEST
SCARECROW	KING OF THE WINGED
TIN WOODMAN	MONKEYS
COWARDLY LION	GLINDA, a Good Witch
TOTO	AUNT EM

Here are the characters. Think about how many actors are needed.

For permission to adapt and reprint copyrighted materials, grateful acknowledgment is made to Plays, Inc., for "The Wizard of Oz, Parts 1 and 2" by L. Frank Baum, adapted by Lynne Sharon Schwartz. Reprinted by permission from *Fifty Plays for Junior Actors*, edited by Silvia E. Kamerman. Copyright © 1966 by Plays, Inc., 120 Boylston St., Boston, MA 02116. This play is for reading purposes only; for permission to produce, write to the publisher.

Going to See the Wizard

NARRATOR: Once upon a time there was a little girl named Dorothy, who lived in Kansas with her uncle Henry, her aunt Em, and her dog, Toto. One day they heard the wailing wind, and they knew that a cyclone was coming. Uncle Henry ran out to take care of the cattle, and Aunt Em ran to a trapdoor in the floor, calling for Dorothy to follow her. At that moment, Toto jumped out of Dorothy's arms and hid under the bed. As Dorothy reached to get him, the house shook so hard that she fell down on the floor. Then the house started whirling around and slowly rose through the air, and was carried miles and miles up into the air. The wind was shrieking loudly, but soon the house felt very calm, and Dorothy crawled into her bed and fell asleep. When she woke up, she found herself in a strange place with Toto beside her.

(Setting: *A field with a house. Two silver shoes can be seen sticking out from under the house.*)

DOROTHY: I wonder where I am! All I can remember is whirling around and around. (*The* Witch of the North *enters with two* Munchkins. *She goes to* Dorothy *and bows.*)

WITCH OF THE NORTH: You are most welcome to the land of the Munchkins. Your house fell on the Wicked Witch of the East, and now she is dead. Those are her two feet sticking out from under the house.

The narrator tells you important details about the characters, setting, and plot.

Here are some details about the setting.

The words in special print tell how the witch moves.

DOROTHY: Oh, dear! I'm terribly sorry! Whatever shall we do?

WITCH OF THE NORTH: There is nothing to be done. She was the Wicked Witch of the East and treated the Munchkins cruelly. Now they are set free and are grateful to you.

DOROTHY: Who are the Munchkins?

WITCH OF THE NORTH: They are the people who live in this land of the East. These are two of my Munchkin friends. (*The* Munchkins *bow to* Dorothy.) I am the Witch of the North.

DOROTHY: Oh, gracious! Are you a real witch?

WITCH OF THE NORTH: Yes, indeed. But I'm a good witch.

DOROTHY: I thought all witches were wicked.

WITCH OF THE NORTH: Oh, no. There were four witches in all the Land of Oz. Two of them, those who live in the North and the South, are good witches. Those who lived in the East and the West were wicked witches. Now that the Wicked Witch of the East is dead, there is just one Wicked Witch left.

1ST MUNCHKIN: Look! The Wicked Witch of the East's feet have disappeared. Only the silver shoes are left.

WITCH OF THE NORTH: She was so old that she dried up quickly in the sun. Now the silver shoes are yours to wear.

2ND MUNCHKIN: These silver shoes have a charm, but we have never known what it is.

Here is Dorothy's goal.

DOROTHY: (*puts on the shoes*) Thank you. Now can you help me find my way back to Kansas?

WITCH OF THE NORTH: (*takes off her crown*) Perhaps we will get a message from my crown to help us. (*reads the message*) The message says, "Let Dorothy go to the Emerald City." Is your name Dorothy?

DOROTHY: Yes. Where is the Emerald City?

WITCH OF THE NORTH: It is in the center of the country, and is ruled by Oz, the Great Wizard.

DOROTHY: How can I get there?

Now Dorothy has another goal. Guess what will happen next.

WITCH OF THE NORTH: You must walk. It is a long, terrible journey, but I will keep you from harm. When you get to Oz, tell him your story and ask him to help you. Goodbye.

DOROTHY: Goodbye, and thank you. (Dorothy *walks around. The* Scarecrow *comes on stage. She walks by the* Scarecrow.)

SCARECROW: Good day.

DOROTHY: Did you speak?

SCARECROW: Certainly. How do you do?

DOROTHY: I'm pretty well, thank you. How do you do?

SCARECROW: I'm not feeling well. It's very tedious being perched up here night and day to scare away crows. If you will help me down, I shall be greatly obliged to you. (Dorothy *helps him down*.) Thank you very much. I feel like a new man. (*The* Scarecrow *stretches*.) Who are you, and where are you going?

DOROTHY: My name is Dorothy, and I am going to the Emerald City to ask the great Oz to send me back to Kansas.

SCARECROW: Who is Oz?

DOROTHY: Why, don't you know?

SCARECROW: No, indeed. I don't know anything. You see, I am stuffed and have no brain.

DOROTHY: Oh, I'm sorry. Emerald City is the place we need to go to see Oz, the wizard.

SCARECROW: Do you suppose that if I go with you, that Oz would give me some brains?

DOROTHY: I cannot tell, but come with me if you like.

SCARECROW: I think I shall. You see, I don't mind my legs and arms and body being stuffed, because I cannot get hurt. But I don't like to be thought a fool. (Dorothy *and the* Scarecrow *walk around the stage. They walk by the* Tin Woodman.)

DOROTHY: I'm sure I heard someone groan. (*looks at* Tin Woodman) Oh! Did you groan?

TIN WOODMAN: Yes, I did. I've been groaning for more than a year.

DOROTHY: What can I do for you?

TIN WOODMAN: Get an oilcan and oil my joints. They are rusted so badly that I cannot move them at all.

DOROTHY: Very well. (Dorothy *gets the oilcan and begins to oil*.)

TIN WOODMAN: Oh, it is wonderful to move again! Thank you so much. I might have stood there always if you had not come along, so you have certainly saved my life. How did you happen to be here?

The Scarecrow wants something.

272

DOROTHY: We are on our way to the Emerald City
        to see the Great Oz. I want him to send me
        back to Kansas, and the Scarecrow wants to
        get a brain.

TIN WOODMAN: Do you suppose Oz could give
        me a heart?

DOROTHY: Why, I guess so. It would be as easy as
        giving the Scarecrow brains.

TIN WOODMAN: If you will allow me to join you, I
        will also go to the Emerald City and ask Oz
        to help me.

SCARECROW: Come along! We'd be pleased to
        have you.

TIN WOODMAN: Look! A lion!

The Tin Woodman
wants something
too.

274

COWARDLY LION: Roar! Roar! (*The* Cowardly Lion *rushes in.* Dorothy *drops* Toto *in her surprise, and the* Lion *runs toward him and tries to bite him.* Dorothy *snatches* Toto *up and then slaps the* Lion *on the nose.*)

DOROTHY: Don't you dare to bite Toto! You ought to be ashamed of yourself. A big beast like you, biting a poor little dog!

LION: (*rubbing his nose*) I didn't bite him.

DOROTHY: No, but you tried to. You are nothing but a big coward.

LION: I know that I'm a coward. But how can I help it?

SCARECROW: What makes you a coward?

LION: It's a mystery. All the other animals in the forest naturally expect me to be brave, for the Lion is thought to be the King of Beasts. I learned that if I roar very loudly, the other animals are terrified and get out of my way.

SCARECROW: But that isn't right. A King of Beasts should not be a coward.

LION: I know it, and it makes me very unhappy. But whenever there is danger my heart begins to beat fast.

TIN WOODMAN: You ought to be glad of that, for it proves you have a heart. I have no heart at all, so it cannot beat fast. But I am going to the great Oz to ask him for one.

SCARECROW: And I am going to ask him to give me brains, for my head is stuffed with straw.

DOROTHY: And I am going to ask him to send Toto and me back to Kansas.

Dorothy sticks up for Toto.

275

Think about what
the Lion wants.

LION: Do you think Oz could give me courage?

DOROTHY: Yes, it would be just as easy for him to help you as it would be to help us.

LION: Then I'll go with you, for my life is unbearable without courage.

DOROTHY: You are very welcome to join us on our long journey to the Emerald City.

A Reader Says

I think that Dorothy was lucky she made some new friends on the way. It would have been scary to be in Oz all alone.

How did you feel about the play?

After You Read

Thinking About What You Read

1. What might have happened if Toto hadn't jumped away when the cyclone came?

2. How was Dorothy helpful to others as she went on her journey to see Oz?

3. How were the Tin Woodman, the Scarecrow, and the Lion alike?

4. How did Dorothy feel about being in such a strange place? Why does she agree to make the journey to see Oz?

Thinking About How You Read

How did knowing what a narrator does help you understand the play?

Sharing and Listening

Tell what you think might happen in Part Two. Will Dorothy and her friends find the Wizard? Will he help them? Give some examples from Part One to help explain why you think something will happen. Listen carefully as other people give their ideas.

Writing

Make a list of things that are strange or unusual about the land of Oz. As you write, think about these questions: What kinds of people live there? What kinds of things happen there?

Even though Dorothy is in an exciting new place, she misses her family in Kansas. She finds out, however, that it's not so easy to get back home.

The Wizard of Oz

Part Two

by Lynne Sharon Schwartz

based on the classic book
by L. Frank Baum

Oz, the Great and Terrible

(Time: *A few days later. They have reached the Emerald City at last.*)

(Setting: *outside of Oz's throne room*)

DOROTHY: I am so glad to be here. I thought we would never arrive.

TIN WOODMAN: Let us hope that the great Oz will see us. (*The* Captain *walks on stage.*)

DOROTHY: Have you asked Oz about us?

CAPTAIN: I gave him your message. When I mentioned your silver shoes, he said he would grant you an audience.

DOROTHY: Thank you. It is kind of Oz to see us.

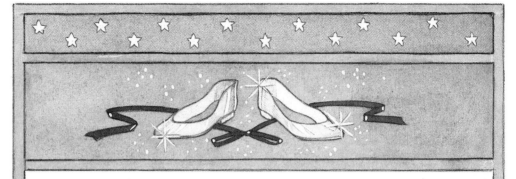

(Setting: *the throne room*)

OZ: I am Oz, the Great and Terrible. Who are you, and why do you seek me?

DOROTHY: I am Dorothy and I have come for help.

SCARECROW: I am only a scarecrow, stuffed with straw, and I have no brains. I want you to give me brains so I may be like a man.

TIN WOODMAN: I am the Tin Woodman, and I have no heart and cannot love. I ask you to give me a heart.

LION: I am a Cowardly Lion, though I am supposed to be King of the Beasts. I have come to ask you for courage.

OZ: (*to* Dorothy) Where did you get the silver shoes?

DOROTHY: I got them from the Wicked Witch of the East when my house fell on her.

OZ: What do you wish me to do?

DOROTHY: Send me back to Kansas to my Aunt Em and my Uncle Henry.

OZ: I will not grant you a favor unless you do something for me in return. Kill the Wicked Witch of the West. She is a tremendously cruel witch.

DOROTHY: I cannot! I never killed anything, willingly, and even if I wanted to, how could I kill the Wicked Witch? If you cannot kill her, how do you expect me to?

OZ: I do not know, but until the Wicked Witch of the West is dead, you will not see Kansas again. (*He turns to the others.*) Help kill the Wicked Witch of the West. When she is dead, come and I will then give you what you desire.

NARRATOR: The next morning the four friends started for the castle of the Wicked Witch of the West. Now, the Wicked Witch of the West had a very powerful eye that could see everywhere. As she stood in front of her castle, she looked out and saw Dorothy with her friends. She was furious to find them in her country, and tried many ways to capture them, but was unsuccessful. Then the powerful witch had one last idea.

(Setting: *in front of the castle of the Wicked Witch of the West*)

WICKED WITCH: The only way left to destroy the strangers is with the Golden Cap. This must be my last command to the Winged Monkeys. (*She says the chant.*) Ep-pe, pep-pe, kak-ke! Hil-lo, hol-lo, hel-lo! Ziz-zy, zuz-zy, zik! (*The* King of the Monkeys *enters.*)

KING OF THE MONKEYS: You have called us for the last time. What do you command?

WICKED WITCH: Go to the strangers within my land and destroy all of them except the Lion. Bring that beast to me, for I shall harness him and make him work like a horse.

KING OF THE MONKEYS: Your commands shall be obeyed. (*lights dim*)

NARRATOR: The Monkeys flew to Dorothy and her friends. First they threw the Tin Woodman in a valley covered with sharp rocks, where he lay battered and dented. Then they caught the Scarecrow and pulled the straw out of his clothes. (*lights up*)

KING OF THE MONKEYS: We have obeyed you. We dare not harm the little girl or the dog she carries with her, for the Witch of the North is protecting her. Your power over our band is now ended. (The King of the Monkeys *exits.* Dorothy *comes in.*)

WICKED WITCH: Dorothy! At last I have you.

282

DOROTHY: You are a very wicked witch for destroying my friends and tying up the Lion, but your power cannot last long. I have a special charm in my silver shoes and it will help me to get rid of you.

WICKED WITCH: The silver shoes! Give them to me!

DOROTHY: No! (Dorothy *seizes a bucket of water and dashes it over the* Wicked Witch, *who begins to shrink*.)

WICKED WITCH: See what you have done? In a minute I shall melt away.

DOROTHY: I'm very sorry, indeed.

WICKED WITCH: Didn't you know water would be the end of me?

DOROTHY: Of course not. How could I?

WICKED WITCH: Well, in a minute I shall be all melted, and you will have the castle to yourself. You have ended my wicked deeds. (*The* Wicked Witch *melts away*.)

283

DOROTHY: Now I must go back to the Emerald City for my reward. But how can I save the Scarecrow and the Tin Woodman and the Lion? Oh, look! There's a magic rhyme in her golden cap! Maybe it will help me. (Dorothy *reads the rhyme.*) Ep-pe, pep-pe, kak-ke! Hil-lo, hol-lo, hel-lo! Ziz-zy, zuz-zy, zik! (*The* King of the Monkeys *enters.*)

KING OF THE MONKEYS: What is your command? We can take you anywhere within the Land of Oz.

DOROTHY: I wish to go to the Emerald City, but I must rescue my friends first.

KING OF THE MONKEYS: We will carry you there, and we will find your friends. Have no fear.

(Setting: Oz's *throne room*)

DOROTHY: That was a good ride.

LION: Yes, how lucky it was that you took that
wonderful cap, Dorothy.

DOROTHY: I wonder where Oz is. I don't see
anyone.

OZ: (*from behind a screen*) I am Oz, the Great and
Terrible. Why do you seek me?

DOROTHY: We have come to claim our rewards.

OZ: What rewards?

DOROTHY: You promised to grant us all our wishes
when the Wicked Witch was destroyed.

OZ: Is she really destroyed?

DOROTHY: Yes, I melted her with a bucket of
water.

OZ: My, how sudden! Well, come to me tomorrow, for I must have time to think it over.

DOROTHY: You've had plenty of time already. You must keep your promises to us. (Lion *roars loudly, and* Dorothy *jumps and drops* Toto. Toto *runs and knocks over the screen, revealing a little old man.*)

TIN WOODMAN: Who are you?

OZ: I am Oz, the Great and Terrible, but—but—I'll do anything you want me to.

DOROTHY: You are Oz?

OZ: I am, but I have been making believe. I'm supposed to be a Great Wizard, but I'm just a common man.

SCARECROW: You're a fake!

OZ: Exactly! But don't speak so loudly. If someone hears you, I shall be ruined.

DOROTHY: But this is terrible. How shall we ever get the rewards you promised?

OZ: My friends, think of me, and the terrible trouble I'm in since you found me out.

SCARECROW: Really, you ought to be ashamed of yourself for being such a fake.

OZ: I am, but being a fake was the only thing I could do. You see, one day I went up in a balloon and I couldn't come down again. I floated miles through the air until I landed here. The people here thought I was a Great Wizard, and I have been good to them. But one of my greatest fears was the Witches. That is why I would promise anything if you would do away with the other Witch. But I am ashamed to say now that I cannot keep my promises.

DOROTHY: I think you are a very bad man.

OZ: Oh, no, my dear. I'm really a very good man, but I must admit I'm a very bad Wizard.

SCARECROW: Can't you give me brains?

OZ: You don't need them. You are learning every day. Experience brings knowledge, and the longer you live, the more you will learn.

SCARECROW: That may all be true, but I shall be very unhappy unless I have brains.

OZ: Then I will try to give you brains. I cannot tell you how to use them, however; you must find that out for yourself. (Oz *goes to cabinet, fills a cup with powder, and pretends to pour it into the* Scarecrow's *head.*)

SCARECROW: Oh, thank you, thank you. And I'll find a way to use them, never fear.

LION: Now, how about my courage?

OZ: All you need is to have confidence in yourself. True courage is facing danger when you are afraid, and you have plenty of true courage.

LION: Maybe I have, but I'm scared anyway.

OZ: Very well, I will get some courage for you. (*holds up glass*) Drink this.

LION: What is it?

OZ: Well, if it were inside of you, it would be courage. Now swallow it.

TIN WOODMAN: How about my heart?

OZ: Why, I think you are wrong to want a heart. It makes most people unhappy.

TIN WOODMAN: I will bear all the unhappiness if you will give me a heart.

OZ: Very well. (*holds up paper heart*) Isn't it beautiful? It is a heart to be proud of.

TIN WOODMAN: Yes, it is, indeed. But is it a kind heart?

OZ: Oh, very kind. It is a heart that any man might be proud of.

DOROTHY: And how am I to get back to Kansas?

OZ: I'll have to think about that for a while.

NARRATOR: Oz finally decided that he and Dorothy should leave in a balloon, but at the moment they were to take off, Dorothy could not locate Toto. By the time she found him, the balloon was already sailing overhead, and Oz could not bring it back. She was very sad, and cried because she thought she would never get back to Kansas. Finally Dorothy found out that Glinda, the Good Witch of the South, might help her.

(Time: *a few days later*)

(Setting: *a room in* Glinda's *castle*)

DOROTHY: This must be Glinda's castle.

GLINDA: I am Glinda, the Good Witch of the South. What can I do for you?

DOROTHY: My greatest wish is to get back to Kansas to my aunt and uncle.

GLINDA: Your silver shoes have wonderful powers. If you had known their power, you could have gone back to your aunt the very first day you came to this country. All you have to do is knock your heels together three times and command the shoes to carry you wherever you wish.

DOROTHY: I shall command them at once. Goodbye, my friends. I'll never forget you.

SCARECROW, TIN WOODMAN, LION: Goodbye, Dorothy. We shall always remember you, too.

DOROTHY: (*knocking her heels together three times*)
Take me home to Aunt Em! Good gracious, here I am in Kansas!

AUNT EM: My darling child! Where in the world have you been?

DOROTHY: In the Land of Oz. And here's Toto. Oh, Aunt Em, I'm so glad to be at home again.

A Reader Says

I think that if Dorothy knew her silver shoes could take her home, she should've stayed in Oz a little longer. She had many new friends and a lot more to see.

How did you feel about the play?

After You Read

Thinking About What You Read

1. What might have caused Dorothy to throw water on the Wicked Witch of the West?

2. How did Dorothy feel about the Wizard after Toto knocked over his screen?

3. What gave people the idea that Oz was a Great Wizard?

4. Why did Dorothy leave Oz so fast after she discovered the magic in her shoes?

Thinking About How You Read

How did understanding stage directions help you understand the characters' feelings and the things they did?

Sharing and Listening

Do you think that it was fair of the Wizard of Oz to tell Dorothy that she had to destroy the Witch of the West before he would help her? Why? Listen carefully as other people give their ideas.

Writing

Imagine you are Dorothy. Write some sentences in your diary that tell who or what helped you get back to Kansas. You might want to describe where the magic shoes came from and how you found out how the shoes worked.

Putting On a Play

Bringing a play to life is a great deal of fun and work. Some plays you might see are very complicated and take a long time to put on. You can put on a play in your classroom, though, that's just as much fun and not too hard to do. Here's a way your class can act out the *Wizard of Oz*.

Many people doing many different jobs have to work together on a play. All these people work under the advice of the director. The director is able to see the play in his mind before it goes on stage. Think of the director as the captain of the team. You might want to get someone older to be the director, like your teacher or aide.

The first thing the director must do is choose the actors and actresses. These are the people he thinks can best act out each character. Think of what part you'd like to play. Remember, there are many roles. You might think acting out the Wicked Witch of the West would be more fun than being Dorothy. Tell the director which character you'd like to be, so he'll know who to choose from.

The next people the director chooses are the people who will make the set. The set is the scenery that will decorate the stage. If you don't have a stage to use, set apart a section of the classroom. The set people are as important as the actors, for they decide exactly how everything will look. There are many ways to construct scenery. For scenes on the path to Oz, you could paint trees and bushes on large pieces of cardboard. They might stand up better if taped to the backs of chairs or desks. You could tape colored paper or carpet to the floor to show different rooms. For thrones like the one Oz sits on, try covering classroom chairs with fancy paper or fabric.

The scenery shouldn't be too complicated, because it's the set person's job to change the set between scenes. Try dimming the lights when you do this. When lights go up, the audience will be surprised at what they see!

Don't forget that you will need props, too. Props are objects that the actors use that aren't really scenery or costumes. The Tinman's heart and the Witch's golden cap are examples of props. If you can't find the right props in the classroom or at home, make them yourself out of cardboard or paper.

The final detail is costumes. How would you dress the Scarecrow or Glinda? Each actor should help the costume coordinators to create his or her own costume. Dorothy might have a dress at home that she could wear. If you don't have the exact costume, try to think of something that looks a lot like it. Can yarn or cut-up paper look like a lion's mane?

Aluminum foil can make a boy or girl into the Tinman. The costumes don't have to look just like the pictures in the book. In fact, just one piece of clothing or even a mask will let the audience know who you are. You'd recognize the Wicked Witch if she were wearing a witch hat instead of a whole costume.

You should practice several times before you act in front of an audience. The director will help you act your part and make sure everything looks right. Professional actors learn their lines by heart, but you can read from the book if you like. The last practice should be in costume and in front of the set. This is called a dress rehearsal.

Now you are ready to invite your friends and parents to watch you act out the *Wizard of Oz*. The audience wants to be made to feel that everything they see and hear on stage is real. If you have worked very hard, you can make Oz seem real.

Not everyone is happy in the same place. Amos and Boris could never live in the same place, but that doesn't mean they can't be best friends.

AMOS
&
BORIS

◆

by William Steig

298

Amos, a mouse, lived by the ocean. He loved the
ocean. He loved the smell of sea air. He loved to
hear the surf sounds—the bursting breakers, the
backwashes with rolling pebbles.

He thought a lot about the ocean, and he
wondered about the faraway places on the other
side of the water. One day he started building a
boat on the beach. He worked on it in the daytime,
while at night he studied navigation.

When the boat was finished, he loaded it with cheese, biscuits, acorns, honey, wheat germ, two barrels of fresh water, a compass, a sextant, a telescope, a saw, a hammer and nails and some wood, in case repairs should be necessary, a needle and thread for the mending of torn sails, and various other necessities such as bandages and iodine, a yo-yo and playing cards.

On the sixth of September, with a very calm sea, he waited till the high tide had almost reached his boat; then, using his most savage strength, he just managed to push the boat into the water, climb on board, and set sail.

The *Rodent*, for that was the boat's name, proved to be very well made and very well suited to the sea. And Amos, after one miserable day of seasickness, proved to be a natural sailor, very well suited to the ship.

He was enjoying his trip immensely. It was beautiful weather. Day and night he moved up and down, up and down, on waves as big as mountains, and he was full of wonder, full of enterprise, and full of love for life.

One night, in a phosphorescent sea, he marveled at the sight of some whales spouting luminous water; and later, lying on the deck of his boat gazing at the immense, starry sky, the tiny mouse Amos, a little speck of a living thing in the vast living universe, felt thoroughly akin to it all. Overwhelmed by the beauty and mystery of everything, he rolled over and over and right off the deck of his boat and into the sea.

"Help!" he squeaked as he grabbed desperately at the *Rodent*. But it evaded his grasp and went bowling along under full sail, and he never saw it again.

And there he was! Where? In the middle of the immense ocean, a thousand miles from the nearest shore, with no one else in sight as far as the eye could see and not even so much as a stick of driftwood to hold on to. "Should I try to swim home?" Amos wondered. "Or should I just try to stay afloat?" He might swim a mile, but never a thousand. He decided to just keep afloat, treading water and hoping that something—who knows what?—would turn up to save him. But what if a shark, or some big fish, a horse mackerel, turned up? What was he supposed to do to protect himself? He didn't know.

Morning came, as it always does. He was getting terribly tired. He was a very small, very cold, very wet and worried mouse. There was still nothing in sight but the empty sea. Then, as if things weren't bad enough, it began to rain.

At last the rain stopped and the noonday sun gave him a bit of cheer and warmth in the vast loneliness; but his strength was giving out. He began to wonder what it would be like to drown. Would it take very long? Would it feel just awful? Would his soul go to heaven? Would there be other mice there?

As he was asking himself these dreadful questions, a huge head burst through the surface of the water and loomed up over him. It was a whale. "What sort of fish are you?" the whale asked. "You must be one of a kind!"

"I'm not a fish," said Amos. "I'm a mouse, which is a mammal, the highest form of life. I live on land."

"Holy clam and cuttlefish!" said the whale. "I'm a mammal myself, though I live in the sea. Call me Boris," he added.

Amos introduced himself and told Boris how he came to be there in the middle of the ocean. The whale said he would be happy to take Amos to the Ivory Coast of Africa, where he happened to be headed anyway, to attend a meeting of whales from all the seven seas. But Amos said he'd had enough adventure to last him a while. He wanted only to get back home and hoped the whale wouldn't mind going out of his way to take him there.

"Not only would I not mind," said Boris, "I would consider it a privilege. What other whale in all the world ever had the chance to get to know such a strange creature as you! Please climb aboard." And Amos got on Boris's back.

"Are you sure you're a mammal?" Amos asked. "You smell more like a fish." Then Boris the whale went swimming along, with Amos the mouse on his back.

What a relief to be so safe, so secure again! Amos lay down in the sun, and being worn to a frazzle, he was soon asleep.

Then all of a sudden he was in the water again, wide awake, spluttering and splashing about! Boris had forgotten for a moment that he had a passenger on his back and had sounded. When he realized his mistake, he surfaced so quickly that Amos was sent somersaulting, tail over whiskers, high into the air.

Hitting the water hurt. Crazy with rage, Amos screamed and punched at Boris until he remembered he owed his life to the whale and quietly climbed on his back. From then on, whenever Boris wanted to sound, he warned Amos in advance and got his okay, and whenever he sounded, Amos took a swim.

Swimming along, sometimes at great speed, sometimes slowly and leisurely, sometimes resting and exchanging ideas, sometimes stopping to sleep, it took them a week to reach Amos's home shore. During that time, they developed a deep admiration for one another. Boris admired the delicacy, the quivering daintiness, the light touch, the small voice, the gemlike radiance of the mouse. Amos admired the bulk, the grandeur, the power, the purpose, the rich voice, and the abounding friendliness of the whale.

They became the closest possible friends. They told each other about their lives, their ambitions. They shared their deepest secrets with each other. The whale was very curious about life on land and was sorry that he could never experience it. Amos was fascinated by the whale's accounts of what went on deep under the sea. Amos sometimes enjoyed running up and down on the whale's back for exercise. When he was hungry, he ate plankton. The only thing he missed was fresh, unsalty water.

The time came to say goodbye. They were at the shore. "I wish we could be friends forever," said Boris. "We *will* be friends forever, but we can't be together. You must live on land and I must live at sea. I'll never forget you, though."

"And you can be sure I'll never forget *you*," said Amos. "I will always be grateful to you for saving my life and I want you to remember that if you ever need my help I'd be more than glad to give it!" How he could ever possibly help Boris, Amos didn't know, but he knew how willing he was.

The whale couldn't take Amos all the way in to land. They said their last goodbye and Amos dived off Boris's back and swam to the sand.

From the top of a cliff he watched Boris spout twice and disappear.

Boris laughed to himself. "How could that little mouse ever help me? Little as he is, he's all heart. I love him, and I'll miss him terribly."

Boris went to the conference off the Ivory Coast of Africa and then went back to a life of whaling about, while Amos returned to his life of mousing around. And they were both happy.

Many years after the incidents just described, when Amos was no longer a very young mouse, and when Boris was no longer a very young whale, there occurred one of the worst storms of the century, Hurricane Yetta; and it just so happened that Boris the whale was flung ashore by a tidal

wave and stranded on the very shore where Amos happened to make his home.

It also just so happened that when the storm had cleared up and Boris was lying high and dry on the sand, losing his moisture in the hot sun and needing desperately to be back in the water, Amos came down to the beach to see how much damage Hurricane Yetta had done. Of course Boris and Amos recognized each other at once. I don't have to tell you how these old friends felt at meeting again in this desperate situation. Amos rushed toward Boris. Boris could only look at Amos.

"Amos, help me," said the mountain of a whale
to the mote of a mouse. "I think I'll die if I don't
get back in the water soon." Amos gazed at Boris
in an agony of pity. He realized he had to do
something very fast and had to think very fast
about what it was he had to do. Suddenly he was
gone.

"I'm afraid he won't be able to help me," said
Boris to himself. "Much as he wants to do
something, what can such a little fellow do?"

Just as Amos had once felt, all alone in the
middle of the ocean, Boris felt now, lying alone on
the shore. He was sure he would die. And just as

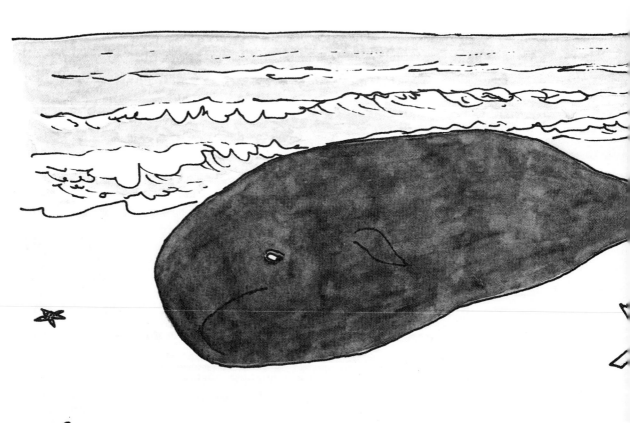

he was preparing to die, Amos came racing back
with two of the biggest elephants he could find.

Without wasting time, these two good-hearted
elephants got to pushing with all their might at
Boris's huge body until he began turning over,
breaded with sand, and rolling down toward the
sea. Amos, standing on the head of one
of the elephants, yelled instructions,
but no one heard him.

In a few minutes Boris was already in water, with waves washing at him, and he was feeling the wonderful wetness. "You have to be *out* of the sea really to know how good it is to be *in* it," he thought. "That is, if you're a whale." Soon he was able to wiggle and wriggle into deeper water.

He looked back at Amos on the elephant's head. Tears were rolling down the great whale's cheeks. The tiny mouse had tears in his eyes too.

"Goodbye, dear friend," squeaked Amos.

"Goodbye, dear friend," rumbled Boris, and he disappeared in the waves. They knew they might never meet again. They knew they would never forget each other.

A Reader Says

I think Amos and Boris should have found a way to visit each other every once in a while. Amos could always build another boat if he wanted to.

How did you feel about the story?

About the Author

William Steig

When William Steig was growing up in the Bronx, he sometimes dreamed of being a writer. When he was 22 years old, he needed a job to help support his parents. That's when he started to work, not as a writer, but as an artist. In time the cartoons he drew for *The New Yorker* magazine became famous and won many prizes.

Mr. Steig was 60 years old before he started writing children's books. He draws all of the pictures for his books. He likes to use bright colors in his pictures.

In *Amos and Boris*, Mr. Steig tries to show the importance of friendship. Although he grew up in a big city, Mr. Steig likes to show his animal characters living happily in the country or in a world filled with adventure and good luck.

Brave Irene is his first book that has people, not animals, as characters. *The Zabajaba Jungle*, which Mr. Steig wrote when he was 80 years old, has a young boy as the hero. In this story, a boy's parents find out that they need his help. Like Steig's other books, this one tells about luck and wonder, and the importance of love and loyalty.

More Books About Other Places

Dorothy and the Wizard of Oz

by L. Frank Baum

You might have thought that Dorothy's adventures in Oz were over. They have just begun! L. Frank Baum wrote many books about Dorothy and the Land of Oz. In this book, Dorothy goes underground and finds the Wizard still traveling by balloon, and it's off to Oz again.

The Girl Who Loved the Wind

by Jane Yolen

Danina's father wants his daughter always to be happy. He keeps sorrow from her by never allowing her to leave his house. But the wind tells her that the world is a big place full of wonderful things to explore.

How Far, Felipe?

by Genevieve Gray

Sometimes people move to other places to find something better. Felipe's family hears of a new land called California and decides to take a chance on going there.

The Story of Jumping Mouse

by John Steptoe

More than anything, Jumping Mouse wants to travel to the far-off land. But his journey does more than just take him somewhere new. It teaches him that he can do more than he ever thought he could.

MAKING ALL THE
CONNECTIONS

Speaking and Listening

The part of the book you have just read is about other places, both new and old. You read about how a familiar place becomes a strange other place to Lobster and Crab. You read how Adan finds out for himself about the other place he has heard of all his life. You read about Dorothy's adventures in Oz. You also read about a mouse named Amos, who, thanks to a whale, learns about life at sea.

Discuss the selections you have read with your classmates. You may want to look at your Reader's Log. Remember to speak slowly and carefully when you give your ideas. Listen carefully as others share their ideas. Use these questions to help you.

1. How are the other places that the stories and the play tell about alike or different?
2. Think about other places that you have visited or wished to visit. How are they like the places you have read about?
3. Discuss with your classmates what the characters in the stories learned about other places.

Reading Something New in Science

Scientists travel to many new and different places. In these other places, they often discover things that no one ever dreamed of. In this article, you will read a description of a scientist's discovery in a place called Indonesia.

Indonesia is a country made up of thousands of islands. It is in the Indian Ocean, from the tip of Asia almost to Australia. It is a country where the weather is very hot and rainy. Great jungle rain forests cover parts of the islands. Scientists come here to discover strange, new forms of plant life.

One of these new forms of plant life was discovered by two scientists, Thomas Raffles and Joseph Arnold. The plant they discovered is the largest in the world. They named it *Rafflesia arnoldii*.

Rafflesia arnoldii looks like a huge head of cabbage. Its petals are like rust-colored velvet with pumpkin-orange spots. It can grow as wide as your teacher's desk and as tall as a five-year-old child. Yet it grows from a seed that is the size of a pea!

This huge plant has no roots. It grows on the roots of wild grape plants. Very few people get to see *Rafflesia arnoldii* in bloom. It grows for almost three years before it flowers. Then it blossoms and dies within a few short weeks.

Thinking About Other Places

Think about the stories you have read. Describe the other places these characters go to. What did they discover when they got there? Use the answers to these questions to help you make place wheels for each of these characters: Lobster, Amos, Dorothy, Adan, and Raffles and Arnold.

In the center of the wheel, put the character and the place he or she visited. On the spokes of the wheel, put some notes about the place. Look at the sample below that has been started for you. Some wheels will have many spokes, others only a few, depending on your ideas.

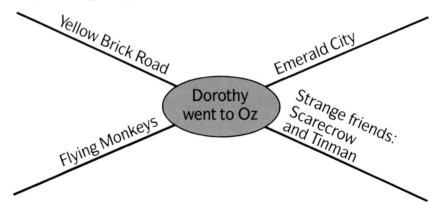

Look back at your wheels. You can see that there are all kinds of places. Think about another place that you have visited. What did it look like? How did it smell? What did you discover there? Maybe you would like to write about your other place. Make a wheel for that place, too. Write your name in the center of the circle. Then complete the rest of the wheel. You can pick more than one place and make a new wheel for each. Later you can decide which one you want to write about.

Writing a Descriptive Paragraph

In this unit, you have read about many places. Now, it is your turn to write a descriptive paragraph about a place. *In Coal Country*, which begins on page 208 of this book, is a good example of descriptive writing. Use these steps to help you write a descriptive paragraph.

Planning

Begin by studying the features of **descriptive writing**.

- Descriptive writing tells about a particular person, place, or thing.
- It uses sensory words to describe. Sensory words tell how something looks, feels, sounds, tastes, or smells.
- It paints a picture with colorful words.

Use comparisons to tell how two different things are alike. Use the wheel you filled out to help you select a place you want to describe.

Composing

Now it is time to write your first draft.

- Brainstorm your ideas with a classmate.
- Use all of your senses to think of words that will help you describe the place you are writing about.
- Think of words that will describe your place in exact detail.

MAKING ALL THE CONNECTIONS

Revising

Now that you have written your first draft, your next step is to revise your writing.

Revising Checklist
- Have I included all the features of a descriptive paragraph?
- Can I add comparisons to make similes or metaphors?
- Can I vary my sentence beginnings?

Phil has written a first draft of a descriptive paragraph. He is going to revise it. Phil uses the Revising Checklist, and uses proofreading marks to show his corrections.

Proofreading Marks

∧ add

℘ take away

≡ capitalize

¶ indent

Phil adds words that describe how the elevator smells.

Phil adds a comparison.

Phil adds a word to describe the music.

The elevator in Mom's office smells ∧*like newspapers and perfume* ~~funny~~. Sometimes its *like a can of sardines* very ℘ crowded. when it is empty I sing out loud with the *traveling* ∧ (musik) that plays there all the time.

Proofreading

Now that you have revised your descriptive paragraph, your next step is to revise punctuation and spelling. The following checklist will help you.

Proofreading Checklist
- Did I indent the first sentence of the paragraph?
- Did I begin each sentence with a capital letter?
- Did I use apostrophes correctly?

Phil looks at his descriptive paragraph again. He checks mistakes in spelling, punctuation, and capitalization. He uses the Proofreading Checklist to help him.

¶ The elevator in Mom's office
like newspapers and perfume
smells ∧ funny. Sometimes it's
like a can of sardines
very crowded. when it is empty
traveling music
I sing out loud with the ~~musik~~
that plays there all the time.

Phil indents the first sentence of the paragraph.

Phil adds an apostrophe.

Phil puts a capital letter at the beginning of a sentence.

Phil fixes a spelling mistake.

Proofread your descriptive paragraph. Ask a classmate to point out parts of your work that can be made better. Listen to your classmate's ideas. Then use them and the checklist to help you revise.

Presenting

Make a neat, final copy of your paragraph. Use these ideas to share it with your class.

Reading aloud: Read your descriptive paragraph to your classmates. You might want to add sound effects, like tapping or whooshing, to your description.

Give a picture talk: Make drawings or collect photographs of the place you described. Show your picture or pictures as you read your description.

This handbook can help you when you write. It gives you proofreading marks to use when changing your writing. It lists grammar and mechanics rules to help you write correctly, and spelling rules to help you check your spelling. It gives information on how to combine sentences to make your writing smoother. You will also find a model to follow when writing a book report.

Use these proofreading marks when you make changes in your writing.

	Marks	Examples
∧	add	What time _did_ ∧ the bus leave?
⅊	take away	Jim ~~walked~~ and I walked to the station.
℘	indent	℘ I am writing you today. . .
≡	capitalize	Jane ṣmith.
/	small letter	William B/ack
⬯	check spelling	They left _yesterday_ (yesturday)
∿	transpose	See͡ign you was nice.

Grammar

Sentences

The rules below show the different kinds of sentences and how to use them.

Rules	Examples
A **sentence** is a group of words that tells a complete thought. A sentence starts with a capital letter and ends with an end mark.	**The boy is walking the dog.**
A **statement** is a sentence that tells something. Put a period at the end of a statement.	A baby dog is called a puppy**.**
A **question** is a sentence that asks for information. Put a question mark at the end of a question.	Which team won the game**?**
A **command** is a sentence that tells somebody to do something. Put a period at the end of a command.	Put the books over there**.**
An **exclamation** is a sentence that shows strong feeling or surprise. Put an exclamation mark at the end of an exclamation.	Look at that beautiful horse**!**
The **complete subject** of a sentence tells whom or what the sentence is about.	**The store's owner** is nice.
The **complete predicate** of a sentence tells what the subject does.	My friend Joe **is from New York**.

Grammar

Nouns

The rules below explain the different kinds of nouns and how to form their plurals.

Rules	Examples
A **noun** is a word that names a person, place, or thing.	The **man** rode his **horse** across the **field**.
A **singular** noun is a word that names one person, place, or thing.	The **girl** will buy one **apple** at the **store**.
A **plural** noun is a word that names more than one person, place, or thing.	Those three **students** won **prizes**.
Add **es** to form the plural of nouns that end in **s**, **ss**, **sh**, **ch**, or **x**.	class**es** box**es** bus**es** bench**es** dish**es**
If a noun ends in a consonant and **y**, change the **y** to **i** and add **es** to form the plural.	cherry cherr**ies**
Some nouns do not follow rules. They change their spelling to form the plural.	foot → feet child → children
A **common noun** names any person, place, or thing. A common noun begins with a small letter.	The **man** lives in the **city**.
A **proper noun** names a particular person, place, or thing. Capitalize the most important words in a proper noun.	**Mary Johnson** lives in **Center City**.

Grammar

Pronouns

The rules below explain pronouns and their correct use.

Rules	Examples
A **pronoun** is a word that takes the place of a noun. A **subject pronoun** takes the place of one or more nouns in the subject part of the sentence. The subject pronouns are **I**, **you**, **he**, **she**, **it**, **we**, and **they**.	Jan likes baseball. **She** likes baseball. The children were here. **They** were here.
An **object pronoun** takes the place of a noun after an action verb. It is found in the predicate part of the sentence. The object pronouns are **me**, **you**, **him**, **her**, **it**, **us**, and **them**.	Marsha called Joe. Marsha called **him**. I found the toy. I found **it**.

Adjectives

The rules below explain adjectives and their correct use.

Rules	Examples
An **adjective** is a word that tells about a noun.	They have a **big** house. She has a **nice** voice.
The words **a**, **an**, and **the** are special adjectives. They are called articles. **A** and **an** are used only before singular nouns.	**A** boy ate **an** apple.

Grammar

Verbs

The rules below tell about the different kinds of verbs and how to use them.

Rules	Examples
An **action verb** is a word that tells what someone or something does.	The girl **fixed** the bike.
A verb in the **present tense** tells about an action that happens now.	Juan **looks** at the sky.
A verb in the **past tense** tells about an action that already happened. Most past tense verbs end in **ed**.	We **looked** for the ball.
The verb **be** is a **linking verb**. A linking verb joins the subject with the words that name or describe it.	She **is** a good singer. Her songs **are** pretty.
A **main verb** is the most important verb in a sentence. A **helping** verb helps the main verb tell about an action. Add **ed** to most main verbs that follow helping verbs.	I **have worked** here before.
Irregular verbs do not form the past tense by adding **ed**.	The family **ate** dinner. I **went** to the game.

Mechanics

Capital Letters and Commas

The following rules will help you use capital letters and commas correctly.

Rules	Examples
Capitalize each important word in a proper noun, such as people's names and titles, and specific places or things.	**M**r. **J**osé **L**opez **M**arch **B**edford **S**treet **R**ocky **M**ountains
Capitalize the first word only in the closing of a letter.	**Y**ours truly, **S**incerely yours,
Use a comma to set off the name of a person spoken to directly in a sentence.	John**,** put the books there.
Use a comma after **yes**, **no**, and **well** when they begin a sentence.	No**,** I wasn't there.
Use a comma after a time order word when it begins a sentence.	First**,** walk two blocks. Then**,** turn left.
Use a comma to separate three or more items in a series.	I bought eggs**,** milk**,** and bread.

Mechanics

Writing Titles

The rules below show how to write titles.

Rules	Examples
Capitalize the first word, the last word, and all important words.	"**T**he **S**kates of **U**ncle **R**ichard" **T**he **W**izard of **O**z
Underline book titles.	<u>The Little Prince</u>
Put short stories and poem titles in quotation marks.	"A Curve in the River" "Dandelion Magic"

Writing Conversation

The rules below show how to write conversation.

Rules	Examples
Enclose a speaker's exact words in quotation marks.	"The play is great," she said.
Begin a quotation with a capital letter.	He said, "**I**t's raining."
Separate a quotation from the rest of a sentence with a comma.	"It's Tuesday**,**" Mickey said.
Put the end marks inside the quotation marks when the quotation is at the end of a sentence.	Sam asked, "What time**?**"

Spelling Strategies

1. You can learn to spell a word in three ways. Which way works best for you?

- ◆ Look at the word. See the letters in it. Picture the word in your mind, remembering the order of its letters.
- ◆ Say the word aloud. Hear the sounds in it. What letter or letters make each sound?
- ◆ Write the word. Practice making the letters. You can also write the words you misspell in a notebook. Write the words correctly. Make the notebook like a dictionary by using one page for each letter of the alphabet. Review your words each week.

2. Always check your spelling when you proofread. Follow these steps:

- ◆ Circle each word you think is misspelled.
- ◆ Write the word again. Does it look right to you?
- ◆ Check in a dictionary if you are not sure.

3. Some words share the same letter pattern. By knowing a pattern, you can spell many words.

- ◆ Words with the **-and** pattern include:
  band   hand   land   sand   stand

4. Many words can be broken into parts. Knowing word parts can help you spell entire words.

- ◆ These words start with the word part **re**:
  reheat   rewrite   repaint
- ◆ These words end with the word part **ly**:
  finally   lonely   quickly

Combining Sentences

Use the following guidelines to help you combine sentences.

Guidelines	Examples
Use the word **and** to combine sentences that have the same meaning part.	John asked questions. + John took notes. = John asked questions **and** took notes.
Use the word **and** to combine sentences that have the same telling part.	Jill walked to the store. + Mary walked to the store. = Jill **and** Mary walked to the store.
Use the word **and** to combine sentences that describe the same person, place, or thing.	The weather is cold. + The weather is damp. = The weather is cold **and** damp.
Use the word **and** to combine sentences that describe the same action.	Mel wrote slowly. + Mel wrote carefully. = Mel wrote slowly **and** carefully.
Use the word **and** and a comma to add one idea to another.	I walked quickly. + I stepped lightly. = I walked quickly**, and** I stepped lightly.
Use the word **but** and a comma to show contrast.	I speak softly. + I sing loudly. = I speak softly**, but** I sing loudly.
Use the word **or** and a comma to show a choice.	We can have apples. + We can have pears. = We can have apples**, or** we can have pears.

Models

A Friendly Letter

Use the models below to help you write and send a friendly letter.

Your letter should look like the one below. Note the heading, the greeting, the body, the closing, and the signature.

> 1636 Santa Cruz Avenue
> San Diego, California 92101
> August 14, 19 ____
>
> Dear Jeanne,
>   It has been so much fun to stay at the beach and play in the waves. Maybe next summer we can take you along and leave my brother at home.
>
>   Sincerely,
>   Maria

heading

greeting

body

closing
signature

To send a letter, you need an envelope and a stamp. Your envelope should look like this:

> Maria Salerno
> 1636 Santa Cruz Avenue
> Miami, FL 33314
>
>
>   Jeanne Clark
>   163 Emerald Court
>   Grapevine, TX
>   76051

return address

receiver's address

Glossary

This glossary can help you find the meaning and pronunciation of some of the words found in this book. Use it when you are having problems with a particular word. The directions below will help you understand how the glossary works.

The pronunciation of each word is shown just after the word, in this way: **ab·bre·vi·ate** (ə brē′vē āt).

The letters and signs used are pronounced as in the words in the pronunciation key below.

The mark ′ is placed after a syllable with a primary or heavy accent, as in the example above.

The mark ′ after a syllable shows a secondary or lighter accent, as in **ab·bre·vi·a·tion** (ə brē′vē ā′shən).

Full Pronunciation Key

a	hat, cap	j	jam, enjoy	th	thin, both
ā	age, face	k	kind, seek	ŦH	then, smooth
ä	father, far	l	land, coal		
		m	me, am	u	cup, butter
b	bad, rob	n	no, in	u̇	full, put
ch	child, much	ng	long, bring	ü	rule, move
d	did, red				
		o	hot, rock	v	very, save
e	let, best	ō	open, go	w	will, woman
ē	equal, be	ô	order, all	y	young, yet
ėr	term, learn	oi	oil, voice	z	zero, breeze
		ou	house, out	zh	measure, seizure
f	fat, if				
g	go, bag	p	paper, cup		a in about
h	he, how	r	run, try		e in taken
		s	say, yes	ə =	i in pencil
i	it, pin	sh	she, rush		o in lemon
ī	ice, five	t	tell, it		u in circus.

A a

a·larm (ə lärm′), sudden fear; excitement caused by fear of danger: *The deer darted off in alarm.* noun.

a·mi·a·bly (ā′mē ə blē), in a pleasant and agreeable manner. *adverb.*

ancient
(def. 1)

an·cient (ān′shənt), **1** belonging to times long past: *In Egypt, we saw the ruins of an ancient temple built six thousand years ago.* **2** of great age; very old: *Rome is an ancient city. adjective.*

ar·range·ment (ə rānj′mənt), **1** a putting or a being put in proper order: *Careful arrangement of books in a library makes them easier to find.* **2** **arrangements**, plans; preparations: *We made arrangements for our trip to Chicago. noun.*

ar·ti·fact (är′tə fakt), anything made by human skill or work, especially a tool or weapon: *Archaeologists study ancient artifacts. noun, plural* **ar·ti·facts.**

as·ton·ish (ə ston′ish), to surprise greatly; amaze: *We were astonished at the force of the wind. verb,* **as·ton·ished.**

auc·tion (ôk′shən), a public sale in which each thing is sold to the person who offers the most money for it. *noun.*

au·di·ence (ô′dē əns), a group of people that sees or hears something: *The audience at the theater enjoyed the play. That television program has a large audience. noun.*

au·to·mat·ic (ô′tə mat′ik), able to work by itself: *We have an automatic dishwasher in our kitchen. adjective.*

ax or **axe** (aks), a tool with a flat, sharp blade fastened on a handle, used for chopping, splitting, and shaping wood. *noun, plural* **ax·es.**

ax or axe

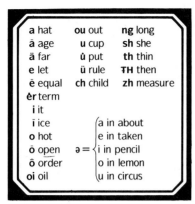

B b

bab·ble (bab′əl), **1** to make sounds like a baby: *My baby brother babbles and coos in his crib.* **2** to make a murmuring sound: *The little brook babbled away just behind our tent.* verb, **bab·bling** *verb, adjective.*

band·age (ban′dij), **1** a strip of cloth or other material used to wrap or cover a wound or injury. *noun.*

banister

ban·is·ter (ban′ə stər), a handrail of a staircase and its row of supports. *noun.*

bick·er (bik′ər), to take part in a noisy quarrel about something unimportant; squabble:

The children bickered about which television program to watch. verb, **bick·ered.**

bit·ter (bit′ər), having a sharp, harsh, unpleasant taste: *This coffee is so strong it tastes bitter.* *adjective.*

bob (bob), to move up and down, or to and fro, with short, quick motions: *The pigeon bobbed its head as it picked up the bread crumbs.* verb, **bobbed.**

boul·der (bōl′dər), a large rock, rounded or worn by the action of water and weather. *noun.*

boulder

Braille or **braille** (brāl), a system of writing and printing for blind people. In Braille, letters and numbers are represented by different arrangements of raised dots and are read by touching them. *noun.* [*Braille* was named for Louis Braille, a blind Frenchman who lived from 1809 to 1852. He invented the system while he was teaching the blind.]

brake (brāk), anything used to slow or stop the motion of a wheel or vehicle by pressing or scraping or by rubbing against: *Dad slammed on the brakes when he saw the stray cat. noun, plural* **brakes.**

brass (bras), a yellowish metal that is made of copper and zinc: *The metalsmith fashioned the candlesticks from brass. noun.*

burlap

bur·lap (bėr′lap), a coarse fabric made from jute or hemp. Burlap is used to make sacks, curtains, wall coverings, and upholstery. *noun.*

bur·row (bėr′ō), **1** to dig a hole in the ground: *The mole quickly burrowed out of sight.* **2** to hide: *She burrowed herself under the covers. verb.*

burst (bėrst), **1** to open or be opened suddenly: *They burst the lock. The trees had burst into bloom.* **2** to go, come, or do by force or suddenly: *Don't burst into the room without knocking. verb.*

C c

cab·in (kab′ən), a small, roughly built house; hut: *a cabin in the woods. noun.*

cel·lo (chel′ō), a musical instrument like a violin, but very much larger and with a lower tone. It is held between the knees while being played. *noun, plural* **cel·los.**

cello

charm (chärm), **1** the power of delighting or fascinating: *The child's charm won our hearts.* **2** a word, verse, act, or thing supposed to have magic power to help or harm people. *noun.*

chi·na (chī′nə), **1** a fine, white pottery made of clay baked by a special process, first used in China. Colored designs can be baked into china. **2** dishes, vases, or other things made of china. *noun, adjective.*

clat·ter (klat′ər), to move or fall with a confused noise; make a confused noise: *The horse's hoofs clattered over the stones. verb.*

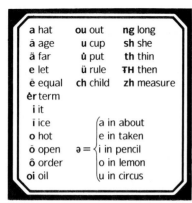

a hat	ou out	ng long
ā age	u cup	sh she
ä far	ů put	th thin
e let	ü rule	TH then
ē equal	ch child	zh measure
ėr term		
i it		
ī ice		a in about
o hot		e in taken
ō open	ə =	i in pencil
ô order		o in lemon
oi oil		u in circus

clus·ter (klus′tər), a number of things of the same kind growing or grouped together: *a little cluster of houses in the valley. noun.*

con·ceal (kən sēl′), to put or keep out of sight; hide: *He concealed the ball behind his back. verb,* **con·cealed.**

con·tent·ed (kən ten′tid), satisfied: *A contented person is happy with things as they are. adjective.*

con·ti·nent (kon′tə nənt), one of the great masses of land on the earth. The continents are North America, South America, Europe, Africa, Asia, Australia, and Antarctica. *noun, plural* **con·ti·nents.**

continent

cork (kôrk), **1** the light, thick, outer bark of a kind of oak tree. Cork is used for bottle stoppers, floats for fishing lines, filling for some kinds of life preservers, and some floor coverings. **2** a bottle stopper made of cork or other material. *noun.*

cot·tage (kot′ij), **1** a small house. **2** a house at a summer resort. *noun.*

cour·age (kėr′ij), bravery; meeting danger without fear: *The pioneers faced the hardships of their westward journey with courage. noun.*

cow·ard (kou′ərd), a person who lacks courage or is easily made afraid; one who runs from danger. *noun.*

co·zy (kō′zē), warm and comfortable; snug: *The cat lay in a cozy corner near the fireplace. adjective.*

cra·dle (krā′dl), a small bed for a baby, usually mounted on rockers. *noun.*

cradle

curve (kėrv), **1** a line that has no straight part. A circle is a closed curve. **2** a bend in a road or river:

The automobile had to slow down to go around the curves. noun.

cus·to·di·an
(ku stō′dē ən), a person in charge; keeper; guardian: *He is the custodian of the library's collection of rare books. noun.*

cy·clone (sī′klōn), a very violent windstorm with circular winds; tornado. *noun.* [The word *cyclone* comes from a Greek word meaning "a wheel," or "a circle." The winds of a cyclone blow in a circle. From the same Greek word come the words *bicycle, motorcycle, tricycle,* and *unicycle.* These words all refer to vehicles with wheels.]

D d

deed (dēd), something done; an act; an action: *To feed the hungry is a good deed. noun, plural* **deeds.**

den·im (den′əm), **1** a heavy, coarse cotton cloth used for jeans,

skirts, and other clothing. **2 denims**, pants or overalls made of this cloth. *noun.*

denims
(def. 2)

des·per·ate·ly
(des′pər it lē), **1** hopelessly; despairingly: *She sighed desperately when she heard the bad news.* **2** extremely; intensely: *The goalie lunged desperately to her right to stop the penalty kick. adverb.*

dig·ni·fied (dig′nə fīd), having dignity; noble; stately: *The queen has a dignified manner. adjective.*

dis·gust·ed (dis gus′tid), filled with dislike or displeasure: *When I struck out again, the coach gave me a disgusted look. adjective.*

dis·play (dis plā′), **1** to show; exhibit: *He displayed his good nature by patiently answering the same question several times. verb.* **2** planned showing of a thing, for some special purpose, exhibit: *Grade 6 had two displays of children's drawings. noun.*

a hat	ou out	ng long
ā age	u cup	sh she
ä far	ů put	th thin
e let	ü rule	TH then
ē equal	ch child	zh measure
ėr term		
i it		
ī ice		a in about
o hot		e in taken
ō open	ə =	i in pencil
ô order		o in lemon
oi oil		u in circus

E e

ech·o (ek′ō), **1** a repeated sound. You hear an echo when a sound you make bounces back from a distant hill or wall so that you hear it again. **2** to be heard again: *The gunshot echoed through the valley.* **1** *noun, plural* **ech·oes; 2** *verb,* **ech·oed**.

ed·i·tor (ed′ə tər), a person who has charge of a publication and decides what will be printed in it: *He is editor of our school paper. noun.*

el·e·gance (el′ə gəns), good taste; grace and beauty that is combined with dignity: *We admired the elegance of the clothes worn to the formal dinner. noun.*

em·bar·rass (em bar′əs), to make uneasy and ashamed; make self-conscious: *She embarrassed me by asking if I really like her. verb,* **em·bar·rassed**.

e·merge (i mėrj′), to come out; come up; come into view: *The sun emerged from behind a cloud. Many facts emerged as a result of a second investigation. verb.*

en·twine (en twīn′), to twine together or around: *Two hearts were entwined on the valentine. verb.*

ex·am·ine (eg zam′ən), to look at closely and carefully: *The doctor examined the wound. verb.*

ex·tinct (ek stingkt′), no longer existing: *The dinosaur is an extinct animal. adjective.*

F f

fake (fāk), **1** something false: *The diamond ring was a fake.* **2** not real; false: *a fake fur, fake money.* **1** *noun,* **2** *adjective.*

fo·rest·y (fôr′əst ē), covered with trees; thickly wooded: *The lake was in the middle of a foresty area. adjective.*

fraz·zle (fraz′əl), **1** to wear to shreds; fray; ravel: *The edges of the rug were completely frazzled.* **2** to tire out; weary. *verb.*

furnace

fur·nace (fėr′nis), an enclosed space to make a very hot fire in. Furnaces are used to heat buildings, melt metals, and make glass. *noun.*

G g

glis·ten (glis′n), to shine; glitter; sparkle: *The stars glistened in the sky. verb,* **glis·tened.**

grime (grīm), dirt rubbed deeply and firmly into a surface: *Soap and water removed only a little of the grime on the coal miner's hands. noun.*

grope (grōp), **1** to feel about with the hands: *He groped for a flashlight when the lights went out.* **2** to search blindly and uncertainly: *The detectives groped for some clue to the mysterious crime. verb.*

grove

grove (grōv), a group of trees standing together. An orange grove is an orchard of orange trees. *noun, plural* **groves.**

guide (gīd), a person or thing that shows the way: *Tourists sometimes hire guides to show them the sights. noun.*

guilt·y (gil′tē), having done wrong; deserving to be blamed and punished: *The jury found her guilty of theft. adjective,* **guilt·i·er, guilt·i·est.**

gur·gling (gėr′gəl ling), flowing with a bubbling sound: *We heard the gurgling of the water over the stones. verb, adjective.*

gutter

gut·ter (gut′ər), a channel or trough along the lower edge of a roof to carry off rain water: *I could hear the water running in the gutter. noun.*

a hat	ou out	ng long
ā age	u cup	sh she
ä far	ù put	th thin
e let	ü rule	TH then
ē equal	ch child	zh measure
ėr term		
i it		
ī ice		a in about
o hot		e in taken
ō open	ə =	i in pencil
ô order		o in lemon
oi oil		u in circus

H h

halt (hôlt), to stop for a time: *The hikers halted and rested from their climb. The store halted deliveries during the strike.* verb, **halt·ed**.

harness
(def. 1)

har·ness (här′nis), **1** the leather straps, bands, and other pieces used to hitch a horse or other animal to a carriage, wagon, or plow. **2** to put a harness on: *Harness the horse.* **3** to control and put to work or use: *Windmills can harness the power of the wind to pump water.* **1** *noun, plural* **har·ness·es;** **2, 3** *verb.*

home·stead (hōm′sted′), **1** a house with its land and other buildings; farm with its buildings. **2** public land granted to a settler under certain conditions by the United States government. *noun.*

honk·er (hongk′ər), goose. *noun, plural* **honkers.**

hor·ror (hôr′ər), a shivering, shaking terror. *noun.*

hu·mil·i·ate (hyü mil′ē āt), to lower the pride, dignity, or self-respect of: *They humiliated me by criticizing me in front of my friends.* *verb,* **hu·mil·i·at·ed.**

hunch (hunch), to draw, bend, or form into a hump: *He sat hunched up with his chin on his knees.* *verb,* **hunched.**

I i

im·mense·ly (i mens′lē), very greatly: *We enjoyed the party immensely.* *adverb.*

in·ci·dent (in′sə dənt), a happening; event: *I saw a*

funny incident on the playground today. noun, plural **incidents.**

in·jus·tice (in jus′tis), a lack of justice; unfairness: *We were angry at the injustice of her decision to punish everyone after one person misbehaved.* noun.

instructions

in·struc·tions (in struk′shənz), directions or orders: *The teachers instructions were clearly understood.* noun.

in·tel·li·gent (in tel′ə jənt), having or showing understanding; able to learn and know; quick at learning. *adjective.*

ir·ri·ta·ble (ir′ə tə bəl), easily made angry; impatient: *When the rain spoiled her plans, she was irritable for the rest of the day. adjective.*

L l

land·mark (land′märk′), **1** something familiar or easily seen, used as a guide: *The traveler did not lose her way in the forest because the rangers' high tower served as a landmark.* **2** a place that is important or interesting: *That building is a historical landmark.* noun.

ledge (lej), **1** a narrow shelf: *a window ledge.* **2** a shelf or ridge of rock. *noun.*

ledge (def. 1)

lev·er (levər or lē′vər), a bar or board used for lifting a weight at one end by pushing down at the other end. It must be supported at any point in between by a fixed part called a fulcrum. *noun.*

lodge (loj), a place to live in; house, especially a small or temporary house: *My aunt and uncle rent a lodge for the summer.* noun.

lone·some (lōn′səm), feeling lonely: *I was lonesome while you were away. adjective.*

lum·ber (lum′bər), to move along heavily and noisily; roll along with difficulty: *The old stagecoach lumbered down the road.* verb, **lum·bered.**

a hat	ou out	ng long
ā age	u cup	sh she
ä far	ů put	th thin
e let	ü rule	TH then
ē equal	ch child	zh measure
èr term		
i it		
ī ice		a in about
o hot		e in taken
ō open	ə =	i in pencil
ô order		o in lemon
oi oil		u in circus

M m

ma·son (mā′sn), a person who builds with stone or brick. *noun, plural* **ma·sons.**

mem·or·y (mem′ər ē), **1** the ability to remember or keep in the mind: *She has a good memory, so she will recall when that happened.* **2** a person, thing, or event that is remembered: *I was so young when we moved that our old house is only a vague memory.* **3** all that a person remembers: *This is the hottest summer within my memory. noun, plural* **mem·or·ies.**

mi·cro·phone (mī′krə fōn), an instrument for magnifying small sounds or for transmitting sounds. Microphones change sound waves into an electric current. Radio and television stations use microphones for broadcasting. *noun.*

mis·er·a·ble (miz′ər ə bəl), very unhappy: *The sick child was often miserable. adjective.*

mon·soon (mon sün′), **1** a seasonal wind of the Indian Ocean and southern Asia. It blows from the southwest from April to October and from the northeast during the rest of the year. **2** a season during which this wind blows from the southwest, usually accompanied by heavy rains. *noun.*

monsoon (def. 1)

mope (mōp), to be dull, silent, and sad: *He has been moping indoors all afternoon. verb,* **mop·ing.**

mus·lin (muz′lən), a closely woven cotton cloth, used especially for sheets. *noun.*

mussel

mus·sel (mus′əl), a water animal that has two hinged parts to its shell. Mussels look like clams and are found in both fresh and salt water. *noun, plural* **mus·sels.**

N n

nar·row (nar′ō), not wide; having little width; less wide than usual for its kind. *adjective.*

nav·i·ga·tion (nav′ə gā′shən), the act or process of navigating; sailing, managing, or steering a ship, aircraft, etc. *noun.*

nudge (nuj), to push slightly to attract attention: *My partner nudged me with her elbow when it was time for me to take my turn. verb,* **nudged.**

nug·get (nug′it), a lump; valuable lump: *The gold nugget glittered in the sunlight. noun, plural* **nug·gets.**

nugget

O o

oc·ca·sion·al (ə kā′zhə nəl), happening or coming now and then, or once in a while: *We had fine weather all through July except for an occasional thunderstorm. adjective.*

or·di·nar·y (ôrd′n er′ē), **1** usual; regular; normal: *My ordinary lunch is soup, a sandwich, and milk.* **2** not special; common; everyday; average: *Our neighbors are ordinary people. adjective.*

ox (oks), the full-grown male of cattle that cannot father young and is used to pull loads or for beef. *noun, plural* **ox·en.**

ox

P p

pas·sen·ger (pas′n jər), a traveler in an aircraft, bus, ship, train, or car: *The bus could carry no more than thirty passengers. noun.*

343

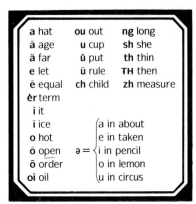

a hat	ou out	ng long
ā age	u cup	sh she
ä far	u̇ put	th thin
e let	ü rule	ᴛʜ then
ē equal	ch child	zh measure
ėr term		
i it		
ī ice		a in about
o hot		e in taken
ō open	ə =	i in pencil
ô order		o in lemon
oi oil		u in circus

peer (pir), to look closely to see clearly, as a near-sighted person does. *verb*, **peered**.

perch

perch (perch), to land and rest; sit: *A robin perched on our porch railing. verb*, **perched**.

per·form·ance (pər fôr′məns), **1** a carrying out; doing: *The firefighter was injured in the performance of his duties.* **2** a thing performed; act; deed: *The child's kicks and screams made a disgraceful performance.* **3** the giving of a play, circus, or other show: *The performance is at 8 o'clock. noun.*

pleas·ant·ly (plez′nt lē), that pleases; agreeably: *a pleasantly cool breeze on a hot day. adverb.*

plunge (plunj), to throw oneself into water, danger, or a fight: *She plunged into the lake to save the drowning swimmer. verb*, **plunged**.

por·ce·lain (pôr′sə lin), a very fine earthenware; china. Porcelain may be so thin that light shines through it. *noun.*

porcelain

priv·i·lege (priv′ə lij), a special right, advantage, or favor: *My sister has the privilege of driving the family car. noun.*

prob·a·bly (prob′ə blē), more likely than not. *adverb.*

proj·ect (proj′ekt), **1** a plan; scheme: *a project for slum clearance.* **2** an undertaking; special assignment. *noun.*

pub·lish (pub′lish), to prepare and offer a book, newspaper, magazine, or other printed material for sale or distribution. *verb*, **pub·lish·ing,** *adjective.*

py·thon (pī′thon), a very large snake of Asia, Africa, and Australia that

python

kills its prey by squeezing. *noun.*

R r

ra·di·ant (rā′dē ənt), shining; bright; beaming: *A radiant smile lit up her face. adjective.*

re·cord·er (ri kôr′dər), **1** a machine or part of a machine that records. **2** a tape recorder. *noun.*

re·quire (ri kwīr′), **1** to need: *We require more spoons for our party.* **2** to demand; order; command: *The rules required us all to be present. verb,* **re·quires.**

re·spon·si·bil·i·ty (ri spon′sə bil′ə tē), **1** a being responsible; sense of duty: *We agreed to share responsibility for planning the party.* **2** thing for which one is responsible: *Keeping my room clean and feeding the cat are my responsibilities. noun, plural* **re·spon·si·bil·i·ties.**

rhi·noc·er·os (rī nos′ər əs), a large, thick-skinned animal of

rhinoceros

Africa and Asia with hoofs and with one or two upright horns on the snout. Rhinoceroses eat grass and other plants. *noun, plural* **rhi·noc·er·os·es** or **rhi·noc·er·us.**

ru·in (rü′ən) **1** very great damage; destruction. *The archaeologist studied the ruins of the ancient city.* **2** bring to ruin; destroy; spoil: *Rain ruined our picnic.* **1** *noun,* **2** *verb,* **ruined.**

rum·ble (rum′bəl), a deep, heavy, continuous sound: *We could hear the far-off rumble of thunder, and knew that the storm was approaching. noun.*

S s

sal·ad (sal′əd), raw green vegetables, such as lettuce and celery, served with a dressing. Often cold meat, fish, eggs, cooked vegetables, or fruits are used along with, or instead of, the raw green vegetables. *noun.*

salad

a hat	ou out	ng long
ā age	u cup	sh she
ä far	ů put	th thin
e let	ü rule	ᴛʜ then
ē equal	ch child	zh measure
ėr term		
i it		
ī ice		⎛ a in about
ο hot		⎜ e in taken
ō open	ə = ⎨ i in pencil
ô order		⎜ o in lemon
oi oil		⎝ u in circus

seam (sēm), **1** line formed by sewing together two pieces of cloth, canvas, leather, and the like: *the seams of a coat, the seams of a sail.* **2** any line where edges join: *The seams of the boat must be filled in or they will leak. noun.*

search (serch), try to find by looking; seek; look for (something): *We searched all day for the lost cat. verb,* **search·ing.**

se·cure (si kyůr′), safe against loss, attack, escape, or danger: *This is a secure hiding place. adjective.*

set·tle·ment (set′l mənt), **1** colony; a group of buildings and the people living in them: *Ships brought supplies to the* colonists′ settlements. **2** a place in a poor, neglected neighborhood where work for its improvement is carried on: *Hull House is a famous settlement in Chicago. noun*

shaft (shaft), a bar to support parts of a machine that turn, or to help move parts. *noun.*

shift (shift), **1** a group of workers who work during the same period of time: *The night shift begins work at 12:30 a.m.* **2** the time during which such a group works: *She is on the night shift this week. noun.*

shiv·er (shiv′ər), to shake with cold, fear, or excitement: *I shivered in the cold wind. verb,* **shiv·ered.**

shiver

shoot (shüt), a new part growing out; young branch: *See the new shoots on that bush. noun, plural* **shoots.**

sig·nal (sig′nəl), a motion or gesture used to mean, stand for, or point out something. *noun.*

skim (skim), **1** to remove from the top: *The cook skims the fat from the soup.* **2** to move or cause to move lightly over something: *You can skim a flat stone over the water if you throw it in a certain way. verb,* **skimmed**.

skit·ter (skit′ər), to move lightly or quickly; skip or skim along a surface: *The rabbit skittered across the road. verb,* **skit·tered**.

slicker

slick·er (slik′ər), a long, loose, waterproof coat, made of oilskin or the like. *I wear a slicker when it's raining. noun.*

slosh (slosh), to splash in slush, mud, or water: *The children sloshed through the puddles. verb,* **sloshed**.

slouch (slouch), to stand, sit, walk, or move in an awkward, drooping manner: *She slouched in her chair. verb,* **slouched**.

smol·der (smōl′dər), to burn and smoke without flame: *The campfire smoldered for hours after the blaze died down. verb,* **smol·dered**.

smolder

smoth·er (smu′ŦHər), **1** to make unable to get air; kill by keeping air from: *The gas almost smothered the coal miners but they got out in time.* **2** to be unable to breathe freely; suffocate: *We are smothering in this stuffy room. verb,* **smoth·ered**.

snatch (snach), to seize suddenly: *The hawk swooped down, snatched the chicken, and flew away. verb,* **snatched**.

sol·id (sol′id) **1** a substance that is not a liquid or a gas. **2** not liquid or gaseous. **1** *noun,* **2** *adjective.*

soot (sut), a black substance in the smoke from burning coal, wood, oil, or other fuel. Soot makes smoke dark and collects on the inside of chimneys. *noun.*

speck (spek), a tiny bit; particle: *A speck in the eye can be extremely annoying. noun, plural* **specks**.

spruce (sprüs), a kind of evergreen tree with leaves shaped like needles. *noun.*

spruce

a hat	ou out	ng long
ā age	u cup	sh she
ä far	ů put	th thin
e let	ü rule	TH then
ē equal	ch child	zh measure
ėr term		
i it		
ī ice		a in about
o hot		e in taken
ō open	ə =	i in pencil
ô order		o in lemon
oi oil		u in circus

sput·ter (sput′ər), to make spitting or popping noises: *fat sputtering in the frying pan. verb,* **sput·tered.**

squall (skwôl), a sudden, violent gust of wind, often with rain, snow, or sleet. *noun.*

stam·pede (stam pēd′), **1** a sudden scattering or headlong flight of a frightened herd of cattle or horses. **2** any headlong flight of a large group: *a stampede of a frightened crowd from a burning building. noun.* [*Stampede* comes from a Mexican Spanish word. It can be traced back to a Spanish word meaning "to stamp."]

starlit

star·lit (stär′lit′), lighted by the stars: *a starlit night. adjective.*

stead·i·ly (sted′l ē), in a regular manner: *She improved steadily. adverb.*

streak (strēk), a long, thin mark or line: *You have a streak of dirt on your face. We saw the streaks of lightning. noun.*

streak

stroll (strōl), to take a quiet walk for pleasure; walk: *We strolled through the park after dinner. verb,* **stroll·ing.**

strut (strut), to walk in a vain, important manner. *verb,* **strut·ting.**

stum·ble (stum′bəl), to slip or trip by striking the foot against something: *to stumble over a stool in the dark. verb,* **stum·bled.**

stur·dy (stėr′dē), strong; stout: *a sturdy child, a sturdy chair. adjective,* **stur·di·er, stur·di·est.**

sus·pi·cion (sə spish′ən), state of mind of a person who suspects; believing to be guilty, false, bad, etc.: *The real thief tried to turn suspicion toward others. noun, plural* **sus·pi·cions.**

sway

sway (swā), to swing or cause to swing back and forth; swing from side to side, or to one side: *The dancers swayed to the music. verb,* **swayed.**

swish (swish), **1** to move or cause to move with a thin, light, hissing or brushing sound: *The whip swished through the air. The child swished the stick.* **2** to make such a sound: *The long gown swished as she danced across the floor.* **3** a swishing movement or sound: *the swish of little waves on the shore.* **1, 2** *verb,* **swish·ing; 3** *noun.*

sym·pa·thet·i·cal·ly (sim′pə thet′ik lē), in a sympathetic way; with kindness: *The doctor spoke sympathetically while bandaging my injured leg. adverb.*

T t

tame (tām), taken from the wild state and made obedient: *a tame bear. adjective.*

tangerine

tan·ge·rine (tan′jə rēn′), the reddish-orange, juicy fruit of a tree grown in warm climates. Tangerines look somewhat like small oranges. *noun.* [*Tangerine* comes from the name of Tangier, a seaport in Morocco, northern Africa. The fruit was originally called "Tangerine orange" because it looked like an orange and was first exported from Tangier.]

ter·ri·fy (ter′ə fī), to fill with great fear; frighten very much: *The sight of a large bear terrified the campers. verb,* **ter·ri·fied.**

thim·ble·ful (thim′bəl fúl), the amount that will fit in a thimble, a small metal or plastic cap worn on the finger to protect it when pushing the needle in sewing; a very small amount. *noun.*

thimbleful

tra·di·tion·al (trə dish′ə nəl), **1** of tradition; handed down by tradition: *Shaking hands upon meeting is a traditional custom.* **2** according to tradition: *traditional furniture.* **3** customary: *A Memorial Day parade is traditional in almost every town. adjective.*

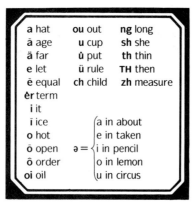

a hat	ou out	ng long
ā age	u cup	sh she
ä far	ů put	th thin
e let	ü rule	TH then
ē equal	ch child	zh measure
ėr term		
i it		
ī ice		a in about
o hot		e in taken
ō open	ə =	i in pencil
ô order		o in lemon
oi oil		u in circus

tread (tred) **1** to set the foot down; walk; step. **2** to beat or press with the feet; trample. *verb,* **tread·ing; tread water:** to keep the body nearly upright in the water by a treading motion of the feet, usually aided by the hands.

trick·le (trik′əl), **1** to flow or fall in drops or in a small stream: *Tears trickled down her cheeks. The brook trickled through the valley.* **2** a small flow or stream. **1** *verb,* **2** *noun.*

trickle
(def. 2)

twitch (twich), to move with a quick jerk. *verb,* **twitched.**

U u

u·ten·sil (yü ten′səl), **1** a container or implement used for practical purposes. Pots and pans are kitchen utensils. **2** an implement or tool used for some special purpose. Pens and pencils are writing utensils. *noun, plural* **u·ten·sils.** [*Utensil* comes from a Latin word meaning "able to be used."]

V v

vi·brate (vī′brāt), to move rapidly back and forth: *A piano string vibrates and makes a sound when a key is struck. verb.*

vol·ca·no (vol kā′nō), **1** an opening in the earth's crust through which steam, ashes, and lava are sometimes forced out. **2** a cone-shaped hill or mountain around this opening, built up of the material that is forced out. *noun, plural* **vol·ca·noes** or **vol·ca·nos.** [*Volcano* comes from the Latin name of Vulcan, the Roman god of fire.]

volcano
(def. 2)

W w

wail (wāl), **1** to cry loud and long because of grief

or pain: *The baby wailed.* **2** a long cry of grief or pain: *The baby woke up with a wail.* **3** a sound like such a cry: *The wail of the coyote was very frightening.* **1** *verb,* **wail·ing; 2, 3** *noun.*

whirl (hwėrl), to turn or swing round and round; spin: *The leaves whirled in the wind.* *verb,* **whirl·ing.**

wide·spread (wīd′spred′), spread widely: *widespread wings.* *adjective.*

wid·ow (wid′ō), a woman whose husband is dead and who has not married again. *noun.*

wiz·ard (wiz′ərd), a man who was believed to have magic power. *noun.*

For permission to adapt and reprint copyrighted materials, grateful acknowledgment is made to the following publishers, authors, and other copyright holders. Every effort has been made on the part of the publisher to locate the copyright holders of these materials. Any unintentional omission of acknowledgment for use of these materials will be promptly corrected by the publisher in future reprint editions.

Mrs. William Weber Coblentz for "Our History Sings," by Catherine Cate Coblentz. Every effort has been made to contact the heirs of the author, and has been to no avail.

Dial Books for Young Readers for "Yagua Days" from *Yagua Days* by Cruz Martel Copyright © 1976 by Cruz Martel. Used by permission of the publisher, Dial Books for Young People. Doubleday & Company, for "Memory" from *Words, Words, Words* by Mary O'Neill. Copyright © 1966 by Mary O'Neill. Reprinted by permission of Doubleday, a Division of Bantam, Doubleday, Dell Publishing Group, Inc.

Farrar, Straus and Giroux for "Amos and Boris." Text and selected illustrations from *Amos and Boris* by William Steig. Copyright © 1971 by William Steig. Reprinted by permission of Farrar, Straus and Giroux, Inc.

Harcourt Brace Jovanovich, Publishers, for "The Little Road" from *Magpie Lane* by Nancy Byrd Turner, copyright 1927 by Harcourt Brace Jovanovich, Inc; renewed 1955 by Nancy Byrd Turner. Reprinted by permission of the publisher.

Harper & Row, Publisher, Inc., for "People" from *All That Sunlight* by Charlotte Zolotow. Copyright © 1967 by Charlotte Zolotow; for "Through Grandpa's Eyes" adapted from *Through Grandpa's Eyes* by Patricia MacLachlan, pictures by Deborah Ray. Text copyright © 1979 by Patricia MacLachlan. Illustrations copyright © 1980 by Deborah Ray; for "Dudley and the Auction" adapted from *Dudley Pippin's Summer* by Philip Ressner, illustrated by Ben Schecter. Text copyright © 1979 by Philip Ressner. Illustrations copyright © 1979 by Ben Schecter; for "The Lobster and the Crab" from *Fables* written and illustrated by Arnold Lobel. Copyright © 1980 by Arnold Lobel. All reprinted by permission of Harper & Row, Publishers, Inc.

Henry Holt & Company for "Steam Shovel" from *Upper Pasture* by Charles Malam. Copyright 1930, © 1958 by Charles Malam. Reprinted by permission Henry Holt and Company, Inc.

Houghton Mifflin Company for "Jumanji" from *Jumanji* by Chris Van Allsburg. Copyright © 1981 by Chris Van Allsburg. Reprinted by permission of Houghton Mifflin Company.

Alfred A. Knopf, Inc., for "A Curve in the River" from *More Stories Julian Tells* by Ann Cameron. Copyright © 1986 by Ann Cameron. Reprinted by permission of Alfred A. Knopf, Inc.; for "In Coal Country" excerpted from *In Coal Country* by Judith Hendershot. Illustrations by Thomas B. Allen. Text copyright © 1987 by Judith Hendershot. Illustrations copyright © 1987 by Thomas B. Allen. Reprinted by permission of Alfred A. Knopf, Inc.

Macmillan Publishing Company for "Very Last First Time" by Jan Andrews, text from *Very Last First Time*. Copyright © 1985 Jan Andrews. Reprinted with the permission of Margaret K. McElderry Books, an imprint of Macmillan Publishing Company; "Gila Monsters Meet You at the Airport." Reprinted with permission of Macmillan Publishing Company from *Gila Monsters Meet You at the Airport* by Marjorie Weinman Sharmat. Text copyright © 1980 by Marjorie Weinman Sharmat.

William Morrow & Co., for "Ramona and the Big Event" pp. 160-161, 163-182 from *Ramona Forever* by Beverly Cleary. Copyright © 1984 by Beverly Cleary. Used by permission of William Morrow & Company; for "The House on Maple Street." Entire text and illustrations from *The House on Maple Street*. Written by Bonnie Pryor. Illustrated by Beth Peck. Text: Copyright © 1987 by Bonnie Pryor. Illustrations: Copyright © 1987 by Beth Peck; for "Long Gone" excerpted from *Zoo Doings* by Jack Prelutsky. Copyright © 1967, 1983 by Jack Prelutsky; for "The Museum" from *What I Did Last Summer*. Copyright © 1984 by Jack Prelutsky. By permission of Greenwillow Books (A Division of William Morrow & Company)

Harold Ober Associates for "Cycle" from *Golden Slippers* by Langston Hughes. Reprinted by permission of Harold Ober Associates Incorporated. Copyright 1941 by Harper & Bros.

G. P. Putnam's Sons for "Old Blue," adaptation of *Old Blue* by Sibyl Hancock, text copyright © 1980 by Sibyl Hancock, reprinted by permission of G. P. Putnam's Sons.

Marian Reiner, for "Growing Up," from *The Little Hill*, poems and pictures by Harry Behn. Copyright 1949 by Harry Behn. Renewed © 1977 by Alice L. Behn. Reprinted by permission of Marian Reiner.

Richard Rieu, for "The Paint Box" by E. V. Rieu.

Yoshiko Uchida, author, for "The Rooster Who Understood Japanese," adapted from *The Rooster Who Understood Japanese*. Text copyright © 1976 by Yoshiko Uchida.

Vanguard Press, for "Pettranella." Reprinted from *Pettranella* by Betty Waterton and Ann Blades. Text copyright © 1980 by Betty Waterton. By permission of Vanguard Press Inc.

Albert Whitman & Company for "Words in Our Hands." *Words in Our Hands* (text only) by Ada B. Litchfield. Copyright © 1980 by Ada B. Litchfield. Adapted by permission of Albert Whitman & Company.

For permission to adapt and reprint copyrighted materials, grateful acknowledgment is made to Plays, Inc., for "The Wizard of Oz, Parts 1 and 2" by L. Frank Baum, adapted by Lynne Sharon Schwartz. Reprinted by permission from *Fifty Plays for Junior Actors*, edited by Sylvia E. Kamerman. Copyright © 1966 by Plays, Inc., 120 Boylston St., Boston, MA 02116. This play is for reading purposes only; for permission to produce, write to the publisher.

Illustration

Anthony Accardo, 23, 25, 27-30; Frank Ahern, 185-187, 189-191, 193; Thomas B. Allen, 209-210, 213, 215-216, 219; Teresa Anderko, 10-11, 20, 47, 90, 117, 172, 197, 234, 260; Jane Chambless, 264-276, 278-292; Carolyn Croll, 102-114; Maureen Cummins, 126-127; Janna Davis, 67; Nancy Didion, 237-244; Mary Young Duarte, 32-33, 86-89; Mark Frueh, 12; Meryl Henderson, 247-251, 253, 255, 257-258; Tom Garcia, 332-351; True Kelly, 137, 139-140, 142-143, 145, 147-148, 150, 152, 155; Elliot Kreloff, 202-206; Rosanne Litzinger, 226; Arnold Lobel, 231; Bob LoGrippo, 164; Scott A. MacNeil, 123; Diana Magnuson, 92, 94-95, 97-99; Barbara Morse, 101; Ben Shecter 168-170; Tom Newsom, 48, 51-52; Michael O'Reilly, 55, 57-60, 62; Stella Ormai, 16-19; Diane Paterson, 294-297; Beth Peck, 128, 131-132, 134; Rodica Prato, 82; Deborah Ray, 35-36, 38-39, 41-42, 44; Vera Rosenberry, 174-175, 177, 179-182; Claudia Sargent, 184-187, 189-191, and 193-194 (borders only), 211, 262-263; Dixon Scott, 198-200; William Steig, 298-301, 303-305, 307-313; Masayo Suzuki, 118-124; Chris Van Allsburg, 65-66, 68, 71-72.

Photography

Courtesy of Houghton Mifflin Co. 76; G. Colliva/The Image Bank 119; Morton Beebe/The Image Bank 121; Pam Haseguax/Taurus Photos 122; E.A. Heinger/Photo Researchers 124; Courtesy of Dell Publishing 156; A. Earl Pamfilie 220; Nancy Crampton 314.